About the Authors

Katie Witkiewitz, PhD, is Associate Professor of Psychology at the University of New Mexico and the Center on Alcoholism, Substance Abuse, and Addictions. She is a licensed clinical psychologist and has worked extensively on the development and evaluation of mindfulness-based treatments for alcohol and drug use disorders.

Corey R. Roos, MS, is a 4th-year clinical psychology doctoral student at the University of New Mexico. He has experience delivering mindfulness-based interventions among clinical populations, particularly individuals with substance use disorders, and he is currently working on developing a mindfulness-based intervention for addictive disorders that can be delivered as a rolling group.

Dana Dharmakaya Colgan, MS, MA, is a 4th-year clinical psychology doctoral student at Pacific University. She has been a student of meditation and mindfulness for two decades and an instructor of meditation and yoga since 2007. She is engaged in the research and clinical application of mindfulness and self-compassion to foster resilience, well-being, and enhanced physiological functioning among first responders.

Sarah Bowen, PhD, is Assistant Professor of Psychology at Pacific University and a licensed clinical psychologist. Over the past 15 years, Dr. Bowen's research, clinical, and training activities have focused on the development, efficacy, and cultural adaptations of mindfulness-based programs. She has conducted clinical trials and trained individuals from diverse populations and settings, both in the US and internationally, including work in prisons, medical and treatment centers, and academic institutions. She is committed to increasing the understanding of and access to mindfulness practice, especially for individuals with logistical, financial, or social barriers to these approaches.

Advances in Psychotherapy – Evidence-Based Practice

Series Editor
Danny Wedding, PhD, MPH, School of Medicine, American University of Antigua, St. Georges, Antigua

Associate Editors
Larry Beutler, PhD, Professor, Palo Alto University / Pacific Graduate School of Psychology, Palo Alto, CA
Kenneth E. Freedland, PhD, Professor of Psychiatry and Psychology, Washington University School of Medicine, St. Louis, MO
Linda C. Sobell, PhD, ABPP, Professor, Center for Psychological Studies, Nova Southeastern University, Ft. Lauderdale, FL
David A. Wolfe, PhD, RBC Chair in Children's Mental Health, Centre for Addiction and Mental Health, University of Toronto, ON

The basic objective of this series is to provide therapists with practical, evidence-based treatment guidance for the most common disorders seen in clinical practice – and to do so in a reader-friendly manner. Each book in the series is both a compact "how-to" reference on a particular disorder for use by professional clinicians in their daily work and an ideal educational resource for students as well as for practice-oriented continuing education.
The most important feature of the books is that they are practical and easy to use: All are structured similarly and all provide a compact and easy-to-follow guide to all aspects that are relevant in real-life practice. Tables, boxed clinical "pearls," marginal notes, and summary boxes assist orientation, while checklists provide tools for use in daily practice.

Mindfulness

Katie Witkiewitz
University of New Mexico, Albuquerque, NM

Corey R. Roos
University of New Mexico, Albuquerque, NM

Dana Dharmakaya Colgan
Pacific University, Hillsboro, OR

Sarah Bowen
Pacific University, Hillsboro, OR

Library of Congress Cataloging in Publication information for the print version of this book is available via the Library of Congress Marc Database under the Library of Congress Control Number 2016961405

Library and Archives Canada Cataloguing in Publication
Witkiewitz, Katie, author
    Mindfulness / Katie Witkiewitz, University of New Mexico, Albuquerque, NM, Corey R. Roos, University of New Mexico, Albuquerque, NM, Dana Dharmakaya Colgan, Pacific University, Hillsboro, OR, Sarah Bowen, Pacific University, Hillsboro, OR.

(Advances in psychotherapy--evidence-based practice ; 37)
Includes bibliographical references.
Issued also in electronic formats.
ISBN 978-0-88937-414-0 (softcover).--ISBN 978-1-61676-414-2 (PDF).--ISBN 978-1-61334-414-9 (EPUB)

    1. Mindfulness-based cognitive therapy. 2. Mindfulness (Psychology). 3. Textbooks. I. Roos, Corey R., author II. Colgan, Dana Dharmakaya, author III. Bowen, Sarah (Clinical psychologist), author IV. Title. V. Series: Advances in psychotherapy--evidence-based practice ; 37

RC489.M55W55 2017   616.89'1425   C2016-907322-X
                                        C2016-907323-8

Cover image © m-imagephotography – iStock.com

PUBLISHING OFFICES
USA: Hogrefe Publishing Corporation, 7 Bulfinch Place, Suite 202, Boston, MA 02114
                Phone (866) 823-4726, Fax (617) 354-6875; E-mail customerservice@hogrefe.com
EUROPE: Hogrefe Publishing GmbH, Merkelstr. 3, 37085 Göttingen, Germany
                Phone +49 551 99950-0, Fax +49 551 99950-111; E-mail publishing@hogrefe.com

SALES & DISTRIBUTION
USA: Hogrefe Publishing, Customer Services Department,
                30 Amberwood Parkway, Ashland, OH 44805
                Phone (800) 228-3749, Fax (419) 281-6883; E-mail customerservice@hogrefe.com
UK: Hogrefe Publishing, c/o Marston Book Services Ltd., 160 Eastern Ave.,
                Milton Park, Abingdon, OX14 4SB, UK
                Phone +44 1235 465577, Fax +44 1235 465556; E-mail direct.orders@marston.co.uk
EUROPE: Hogrefe Publishing, Merkelstr. 3, 37085 Göttingen, Germany
                Phone +49 551 99950-0, Fax +49 551 99950-111; E-mail publishing@hogrefe.com

OTHER OFFICES
CANADA: Hogrefe Publishing, 660 Eglinton Ave. East, Suite 119-514, Toronto, Ontario, M4G 2K2
SWITZERLAND: Hogrefe Publishing, Länggass-Strasse 76, CH-3000 Bern 9

Hogrefe Publishing
Incorporated and registered in the Commonwealth of Massachusetts, USA, and in Göttingen, Lower Saxony, Germany

Printed and bound in the USA

ISBN 978-0-88937-414-0 (print) • ISBN 978-1-61676-414-2 (PDF) • ISBN 978-1-61334-414-9 (EPUB)
http://doi.org/10.1027/00414-000

Preface

The theories, understandings, and practices reviewed in this book are rooted in a rich and ancient tradition. We want to provide a brief and simplified introduction to contemporary applications of "mindfulness" as delivered within secularized mindfulness-based interventions. This is by no means a complete account of mindfulness practices, and can at best provide a very broad overview to a longstanding, multifaceted, and now multi-cultured system of understanding and practice. This book is intended for those who are curious about the roots and practices of mindfulness, and the directions of current science and clinical applications. It is a starting place for readers interested in learning about an extraordinarily rich and honored practice, and the ways in which mindfulness training has become foundational to many evidenced-based approaches in psychology.

We dedicate this book to Dr. G. Alan Marlatt (1941–2011) who provided the foundation for an evidenced-based and integrated mindfulness approach to the prevention of addictive behavior relapse. We also dedicate this work to the many research participants and clients who continually inspire us and remind us of the importance of the dissemination of mindfulness-based interventions. We would also like to acknowledge Dr. Danny Wedding, who provided invaluable comments and editorial feedback, and Dr. Linda Sobell, who invited us to author this book.

KW dedicates this book to her current and former students who continue to support this work.

CRR dedicates this book to his parents, Richard and Cindy, who have taught him what it means to be kind and compassionate.

DDC dedicates this book to Don, whose bountiful love, support, and quiet patience never cease to amaze her.

SB dedicates this book to her many teachers, in their many forms, who continue to point her towards perseverance, authenticity, and growth.

Contents

1

Description

1.1   Terminology and Definitions

Mindfulness is often translated as _seeing with discernment_. Mindfulness practice is a form of mental training that enhances one's ability to nonjudgmentally attend to the present moment: a phenomenological process oriented toward a gradual understanding of one's direct experience (Goldstein, 1980). As a type of consciousness, it has the quality of a presence of mind with a certain stability of focus (Bodhi, 2011). Increased mindfulness can afford an individual freedom from misperceptions, rigid and problematic thinking patterns, and self-imposed limitations that interfere with optimal mental and physical health. Mindfulness can also be understood by its contrast to restlessness, forgetfulness, behavioral and cognitive automaticity, and states of mind in which attention is focused elsewhere, such as preoccupation with memories, anticipation of the future, rumination, and worry (Brown & Ryan, 2003).

Western psychology often conceptualizes mindfulness as a collection of techniques, but also as a psychological process, a psychological trait, and the positive emotional outcomes of the practice itself (Hayes & Wilson, 2003). A commonly cited definition by Jon Kabat-Zinn (2002) is "the awareness that emerges by way of paying attention on purpose, in the present moment, and nonjudgmentally to the unfolding of experience, moment by moment" (p. 732). Similarly, two salient components of mindfulness are described by Bishop and colleagues as (a) the intentional regulation of attention to and awareness of the present moment and (b) a nonjudgmental and curious willingness to experience the content (thoughts, sensations, and feelings) of the present moment (Bishop et al., 2004). Shapiro and colleagues further distinguished attentional focus from intention (purpose of the focus) in her three factor model of attention, intention, and attitude (Shapiro, Carlson, Astin, & Freedman, 2006). Baer and colleagues proposed a five facet model of mindfulness characterized by observing, describing, nonreactivity to inner experience, nonjudging of inner experience, and acting with awareness (Baer, Smith, Hopkins, Krietemeyer, & Toney, 2006). While additional models have been proposed, most of these contemporary models contain three essential elements: awareness of the present moment, attentional allocation, and the cultivation of specific qualities pertaining to the attention and awareness of the present moment.

Foremost of the processes of fostering mindfulness is developing a clear awareness of one's present internal or _personal_ experiences, including thoughts, emotions, sensations, and behaviors, as well as attention to perception of elements in the surrounding environment, such as sights and sounds. For this reason, some have defined mindfulness as _bare attention_, or

In Western psychology, there are many different definitions and conceptualizations of mindfulness

There are three essential elements of contemporary mindfulness models

Awareness of experience is a fundamental aspect of mindfulness *pure* or *lucid* awareness (Dass & Goleman, 1990). These terms suggest that mindfulness reveals what is occurring before or beyond ideas, judgements, or analyses. The Zen metaphor of a polished mirror, through which the mind is able to simply reflect what passes before it, unbiased by conceptual thought about what is taking place, describes this state of pure awareness. This can be contrasted with *automatic* cognitive and behavioral reactions that occur without conscious awareness. Awareness is often at the forefront of contemporary explanations of and training in mindfulness, and is indeed a necessary and foundational element of mindfulness; however, most (if not all) individuals' awareness is shaped by conditioning, and contains both valence (positive or negative) and evaluation. Therefore, awareness may be better understood as a precondition to, or elemental factor for, mindfulness, rather than its complete definition.

A second inherent process of mindfulness is attentional allocation, which involves sustained attention, monitoring, and attentional shifting (Garland, Froeliger, & Howard, 2014; Malinowski & Lim, 2015). As an individual attempts to attend to an object (the breath, bodily sensations, sustained attention), one is also acknowledging discursive thoughts and emotions that may arise (a process of *monitoring*). The ability to notice getting "caught up" in thoughts or emotions, and subsequently returning to the object of attention, requires a purposeful and fluid shifting of attention (*attentional shifting*). As the mind wanders off into concerns about the future, ruminations about events that occurred in the past, or evaluations of the present moment, the mindfulness practitioner notices these processes and then gently redirects attention back to the sensations and experiences occurring in the present moment.

Mindfulness practice cultivates nonreactivity and nonjudgment

A third, and perhaps most important, aspect of mindfulness is the cultivation of particular qualities of awareness. Attitudes that exemplify this quality include kindness, curiosity, acceptance, nonreactivity, and equanimity. A kind, curious, and nonreactive awareness is developed so that one simply notices the object, or series of emerging objects, and the secondary evaluations and appraisals that occur. With continued practice, this nonreactive awareness eventually allows for the de-automatization of habitual reactions to the present moment and the associated secondary appraisals, predictions, analyses, critiques, or judgments about what has or is taking place. This process can be understood as the further development and temporal extension of bare attention, thereby adding clarity and depth to the typically shorter periods, or momentary flashes, of time occupied by bare attention (Keng, Smoski, & Robins, 2011; Olendzki, 2011).

Furthermore, the meditator practices meeting all internal experiences that arise – positive, negative, or neutral – with equal interest and equanimity. This is in contrast to the typical human tendency to seek and hold onto pleasure and to avoid and escape from discomfort. Instead, the mindful practitioner remains aware of what is happening internally, with an even and unbiased deportment, as if gazing upon the internal landscape without interference (Desbordes et al., 2014). It is purported that it is only when one can regard an experience, or object of attention, with a balanced objectivity that one is free from emotional agitation, and the understanding of the experience or object is potentially transformative (Olendzki, 2011). This is reflective of the elements of awareness, allocation of attention, and a nonjudgmental or equanimous stance toward all experience. Grossman (2015) describes this coalescing of awareness and attention with a particular set of attitudes as an act of unbiased, open-hearted, equanimous experience of perceptible events and processes as they unfold from moment to moment (sensations, perceptions, thoughts, emotions, imagery).

Mindfulness meditation differs from concentration-based meditation practices, though historically the two practices are intimately interwoven (Anālayo, 2004; Rinpoche, 2011). Concentration practices, also described as focused practices, require restricting one's attention to a single object, such as the breath, a repeated word or phrase (mantra), a sensation, or visualization. When the mind wanders during a concentration practice, attention is brought back to the object of attention with little or no investigation of the *distraction*. A concentration practice calms and stabilizes the wandering and distracted mind, and has historically been considered a perquisite for a more advanced mindfulness practice.

Preliminary concentration practices have several advantages. First, while attempting to focus the restless and wandering mind, one may become more aware of the mind's tendency to judge simple sensation (Sayadaw, 1994). Having noticed the mind's frequent tendency to judge and evaluate, an individual can become increasingly aware of the mind as an intermediary or secondary interpreter (Dreeben, Mamberg, & Salmon, 2013). Second, the calm mental state that results from these practices provides the foreground from which one is most easily able to recognize and perceptually distinguish thoughts and feelings about sensation from direct perception of sensation. The ability to distinguish between sensation and cognition opens the opportunity to remain longer with the pure sensory experience before attention is once again overtaken by language-based judging, evaluation, and comparing. Third, a concentration practice creates the mental state in which delight and rapture are most acutely experienced (Dhargyey, 1974).

> Concentration practices provide a foundation for training in mindfulness

With a concentration practice that has stabilized and strengthened attentional allocation processes, participants then proceed to the practice of mindfulness: expanding the awareness from the restricted, focused attention to encompass an open, receptive, nonjudgmental awareness or observation of the constantly changing stream of internal and external stimuli as they arise and dissolve, moment by moment. This expanded, nonjudgmental, nonreactive awareness embraces all thoughts, emotions, physical sensations, memories, fantasies, perceptions, and urges with a sense of equanimity and balance. Therefore, mind wandering is simply another event to witness (Olendzki, 2011).

Mindfulness practice cultivates an awareness of one's own experiences without attachment or investment in what or how particular experiences occur. The advantage of this perspective is that the self is experienced as an arena in which the internal content of consciousness is not threatening (Hayes, Pistorello, & Levin, 2012). With practice, individuals begin to experience thoughts and emotions as temporary states, rather than as identifying characteristics, providing a sense of steadiness. In this way, mindfulness has been referred to as the ground of mental function or *choiceless awareness* (Kabat-Zinn, Lipworth, & Burney, 1985). Therefore, a concentration practice that develops the capacity to cultivate attention in a more direct and deliberate manner can help the mindfulness practitioner begin to discern and understand the nature of the mind. With time and practice, wisdom arises.

Curiosity and acceptance are core skills in mindfulness training

Cultivating a deliberate and focused awareness with acceptance and curiosity counteracts the tendency toward experiential avoidance, alters the relationship and interaction with internal content, and can create a sense of spaciousness around whatever is being experienced or observed; the dynamic, constantly changing experience is simply *noticed*. In this way, an individual becomes familiar with, and perhaps even friendly toward, the nature and habits of the mind. One is then empowered to respond to the present-moment experience rather than habitually, and often unconsciously, reacting. This can allow for a broader, and potentially more skillful, behavioral repertoire, freeing one from the habitual cognitive, emotional, and behavioral patterns that perpetuate suffering, providing a path toward peace and contentment.

Humans tend to respond on *automatic pilot*

Four core assumptions underlie the construct of mindfulness (Bodhi, 2011). The first assumption suggests that individuals are ordinarily unaware of their moment-to-moment experience, operating in an *automatic pilot* mode. This automatic pilot mode, also known as *mind wandering*, consists of daydreaming, contemplating the future, reliving the past, or general rumination. A recent study found mind wandering was reported to occur almost 50% of the time, regardless of what subjects were doing (Killingsworth & Gilbert, 2010).

The second assumption is that individuals are capable of developing sustained attention to mental, emotional, and physical experience and increasing the fluidity and ease of attentional shifting and cognitive flexibility. Meta-analyses have demonstrated the effectiveness of mindfulness training on enhancing attentional allocation and cognitive and psychological flexibility (Chiesa & Serretti, 2011; Slagter, Davidson, & Lutz, 2011).

A commitment to a regular, formal mindfulness practice is a critical component in mindfulness training

The third assumption suggests that a regular practice is necessary to develop this skill. While there are some Western approaches that suggest formal practice is not necessary (Langer, 1989), researchers have found that formal and informal mindfulness practices result in cognitive, affective, behavioral, and neurological changes (Hölzel et al., 2010; Hölzel, Lazar, et al., 2011; Jha, Krompinger, & Baime, 2007; Lutz, Jha, Dunne, & Saron, 2015) and have lasting effects (Rogers, Christopher, & Bilgen-Sunbay, 2013).

The fourth and final assumption suggests that moment-to-moment awareness of true experience provides a more vibrant and meaningful sense of life. Correlational studies have documented the associations among trait and state mindfulness and wellbeing, quality of life, and positive affect, and outcomes studies have demonstrated the positive impact on wellbeing and quality of life (Keng et al., 2011). Furthermore, mind wandering has been inversely correlated with levels of self-reported happiness (Killingsworth & Gilbert, 2010). These four assumptions, now largely supported by empirical evidence, have greatly influenced the integration of mindfulness and meditation into Western medicine, psychology, and education.

1.2   Historical Roots of Mindfulness

1.2.1   Ancient and Contemporary Teachings of the Buddha

The essence of mindfulness lies at the heart of many ancient and contemporary traditions and teachings. Although these practices are indeed seen across many cultures and contexts, mindfulness is typically taught as a secular practice in modern healthcare settings. Teaching these practices in such a way may make them more available to individuals who are interested in training their minds, but who do not wish to study or ascribe to Buddhism. However, it is helpful to have at least a basic understanding of these practices in the context of Buddhism, in which they were articulated with great intellectual precision by the Buddha over 2,500 years ago in two principal discourses: the *Ānāpānasati Sutta* and the *Satipaṭṭhāna Sutta* (Anālayo, 2004).

> Contemporary mindfulness practices are based on Buddhist teachings over 2500 years old

Rooted in ancient yogic practices, these teachings offered a process-oriented view of experience as a series of interdependent, cognitive events arising and dissolving each moment as the sense organs encounter incoming environmental data, with which the mind then constructs a world of meaning to interpret and respond to – cognitively, emotionally, and behaviorally (Olendzki, 2011). Over the last two millennia, the temporal and geographical dissemination of the teachings of Buddhism has produced a plethora of theories and commentaries for traversing a path for systematic mental training and human development. Consequently, mindfulness, even within Buddhism and its various schools, is subject to varied understandings and applications (Purser & Milillo, 2015).

Though mindfulness is subject to various understandings and applications, Buddhist scholars agree that the ultimate goal of mindfulness is to eliminate the causes of suffering – rooted in ignorance, attachment, and aversion – for all sentient beings. This in-depth mind development is purported to alleviate, and ultimately eliminate, suffering by fostering sustainable changes in one's cognitive and emotional states that, subsequently, lead to changes in more permanent and stable behavioral and psychological traits (Dhargyey, 1974). The conceptual framework provided to lead individuals from suffering was the *Four Noble Truths*: (a) definition of suffering, (b) the origins of suffering, (c) the cure for suffering, (d) and the path that leads to the end of suffering, known as the *Noble Eightfold Path*. The eight factors of the path to liberation can be grouped into three essential elements of Buddhist practice: (1) the development of ethical discipline, integrity, and virtues (Right Speech, Right Action, Right Livelihood); (2) mental discipline (Right Effort, Right Mindfulness, Right Concentration); and (3) wisdom (Right View, Right Thought/Intention).

Right Mindfulness is the seventh path factor situated in-between Right Effort and Right Concentration. Mindfulness or *sati* (*smṛti* in Sanskrit) is derived from the verb *to remember* or the act of *calling to mind* (Ṭhānissaro, 2012). A wide range of meanings have been associated with *sati*, such as recollection (*anussati*), recall (*patissati*), remembrance (*saranata*), keeping in mind (*dharanata*), absence of floating (*apilapamata*), and absence of forgetfulness (*asammussanata*) (Gethin, 2011; Purser & Milillo, 2015). These early definitions reflect the philosophy that *sati* is not the equivalent of the function of memory, but instead, an active, purposeful, and particular way of attending

> In Buddhist teachings, mindfulness is part of the path that leads to the end of suffering, known as the Noble Eightfold Path

and remembering. Thus, the historical understanding of mindfulness is not merely a passive and nonjudgmental attentiveness or awareness exclusively to the present moment, but an actively engaged and discerning awareness that is capable of remembering and knowing skillful, as well as unskillful, phenomena and behaviors of the past and in the present, with the intended purpose of abandoning those that lead to suffering and distress (Gethin, 2011; Purser & Milillo, 2015; Ṭhānissaro, 2012).

This watchful, nonreactive receptivity forms the foundation for *satipatthana,* usually translated as clear comprehension: a middle path which neither suppresses the content of the present moment experience, nor habitually reacts. Instead, through the development of clear comprehension, one first develops a basic knowing of what is happening in the present moment, which subsequently may lead to a discriminative ability to discern wholesome from unwholesome thoughts and behaviors within the present moment. Clear comprehension, therefore, helps inform, shape, and support the development of mindfulness by decreasing desire for and attachment to afflictions that disturb the peacefulness of the mind. Reciprocally, mindfulness increases the ability to act and respond in an informed manner, and it diminishes the likelihood of being carried away by emotions or conditioned responses.

Explicit instructions on how to develop mindfulness are found in the *Satipaṭṭhāna Sutta,* a highly revered discourse of the Buddha, in which the practice of mindfulness is divided into mindfulness and contemplation of: (1) bodily sensations, (2) neutral, pleasant, or unpleasant feelings, (3) mind and mental processes of anger, lust, and delusion, and (4) mind objects or phenomena. These four foundations are frames of reference and are usually taught sequentially until the individual becomes skilled enough to expand his/her awareness to encompass the entirety of the constantly changing present moment. While practicing mindfulness of the four foundations, one becomes aware and contemplates the arising and dissolving of phenomena in the stream of present moment experience. The practice progressively develops from a refining of attention and awareness (*Samatha*) into a deep analytical probing and insight (*Vipassana*). With effort and dedication, mindfulness states become more frequent and continuous. Steadiness of awareness and attention and a firmly established Right View assist to diminish opportunities for concepts, ideas, and associated emotions to be blindly or automatically tacked onto bare facts. Such steadiness also facilitates the recognition of being caught up in conceptual thoughts or emotions rooted in past experience or anticipated futures. Subsequently, the mindful practitioner then returns to an awareness of what is currently taking place. This cultivation of mindfulness leads to the transformation of the human mind by diminishing, and eventually eliminating, destructive mental and emotional states (Anālayo, 2004).

1.2.2   Translation of Buddhist Practices Into Western Science and Medicine

The scientific study of meditation has a relatively short history in relation to its age

Western science's interest in the use of meditative techniques began to grow among clinicians in the early 1960s. Beginning in the early 1970s, there was a surge of interest in and research on transcendental meditation (TM), a concentrative meditation technique popularized by Maharishi Mahesh Yogi (Wallace, 1970). The practice of TM was found to be associated with reductions in indicators of physiological arousal such as oxygen consumption, carbon dioxide elimination, and respiratory rate (Benson, Marzetta, Rosner, & Klemchuk, 1974). Studies on meditation continued to flourish as cardiologist Herbert Benson used the practice of meditation to treat heart disease and evoke the relaxation response (Benson & Klipper, 1976). In 1977, the America Psychiatric Association called for an examination of the clinical effectiveness of meditation and for a decade most of the research investigated the clinical effects of concentration practices (Germer, Siegel, & Fulton, 2013).

Application of mindfulness meditation as a Western, secularized treatment intervention largely began with the work of Jon Kabat-Zinn in the late 1980s, in which he explored the use of mindfulness meditation in treating patients with chronic pain, now popularly known as mindfulness-based stress reduction (MBSR; Kabat-Zinn et al., 1985). Multiple treatment protocols that aimed to integrate mindfulness into psychotherapy approaches soon followed with successful results. Dialectical behavior therapy (DBT; Linehan, 1993a, 1993b) was the first protocolled, evidence-based psychotherapy to formally incorporate mindfulness as a core component. The mindfulness skills in DBT are described as a behavioral translation of a Zen practice. Originally developed for borderline personality disorder and related problems, DBT has also been found to be a useful adjunct to empirically supported post-traumatic stress disorder treatments to enhance emotion regulation and tolerance for distress (Wagner & Linehan, 2007). Similarly, acceptance and commitment therapy (ACT; Hayes, Strosahl, & Wilson, 1999) has mindfulness as one of its core components. ACT is a transdiagnostic approach developed out of relational frame theory. The goal of ACT is to increase psychological flexibility and empower value-driven behavior change.

The next generation of evidence-based psychotherapies shifted from mindfulness-based skills as one of several therapeutic components to formal mindfulness practice as the foundation of the treatment. Based on the content and structure of MBSR, mindfulness-based cognitive therapy (MBCT; Teasdale et al., 2002) draws upon mindfulness practices skills and cognitive-behavior therapy techniques with the goal of reducing the risk of depressive relapse. Mindfulness-based relapse prevention (MBRP; Bowen, Chawla, & Marlatt, 2011; Witkiewitz, Marlatt, & Walker, 2005) integrates mindfulness meditation practices with cognitive-behavioral strategies to support recovery from alcohol and substance use disorders.

There is a growing body of robust evidence from randomized clinical trials (RCTs) demonstrating the effectiveness of mindfulness-based interventions (MBIs) in improving a range of physical and psychological outcomes in comparison to control conditions. There is scientific evidence to support the beneficial effects of MBIs on medical conditions, including Type 2 diabetes (Rosenzweig et al., 2007), fibromyalgia (Grossman, Tiefenthaler-Gilmer, Raysz, & Kesper, 2007), rheumatoid arthritis (Pradhan et al., 2007), and attention-deficit hyperactivity disorder (Mitchell, Zylowska, & Kollins, 2015). Clinical efficacy and durability have been shown for eating disorders (Wanden-Berghe, Sanz-Valero, & Wanden-Berghe, 2010), insomnia (Ong & Sholtes, 2010), and substance use disorders (Bowen et al., 2011). Recent meta-

Numerous MBIs have been developed for a wide range of conditions with many being evaluated scientifically

analyses estimated small- to medium-sized treatment effects for the impact of mindfulness training on symptoms of stress, anxiety, depression (Hofmann, Sawyer, Witt, & Oh, 2010), and psychosis (Khoury, Lecomte, Gaudiano, & Paquin, 2013). Additionally, MBIs have been shown to inhibit unhealthy adaptations or coping responses to chronic stress, such as smoking, decreased exercise, and poor sleep (Grossman, Niemann, Schmidt, & Walach, 2004).

1.3   Eastern and Western Variations

Western and Buddhist conceptualizations of mindfulness focus on alleviating suffering

Both Eastern and Western perspectives on mindfulness share an overarching intention to alleviate suffering, and there is significant overlap in their intentions and methodologies; cultivating mindfulness helps keep the mind grounded in the present moment, decreases reactivity and judgment to what is experienced, and changes the relationship to the internal landscape, as a means to reduce suffering and increase well-being. Relatedly, both conceptualizations acknowledge that one's experience of the world is largely dependent on perception. Eastern and Western conceptions of mindfulness are also similar in their views of the interactive relationship between the body and mind, whereas behavioral, cognitive, affective, and biological experiences can be influenced through the practice of mental training. Furthermore, both perspectives postulate that mindfulness cultivates learning and fosters the possibility of change and the adoption of new perspectives. Despite these foundational shared views, there are clear differences. The question of areas of commonality and divergence is not without controversy (Christopher, Charoensuk, Gilbert, Neary, & Pearce, 2009; Grossman, 2011; Lindahl, 2015; Purser & Milillo, 2015).

The first and perhaps most notable inconsistency between the Western and Buddhist conceptualization of mindfulness is regarding their objectives. The Western scientific community has adopted mindfulness practice as a therapeutic technique to provide individuals symptomatic relief and enhanced wellbeing and quality of life. This general aim may center on alleviation of depression, anxiety, chronic pain, chronic disease, problematic substance use, or emotional dysregulation. Alternatively, Buddhism arose as a solution to the inherent suffering in life; therefore, the ultimate goal of mindfulness is not only to alleviate specific areas of suffering, but to eliminate the *root cause* of suffering – ignorance, attachment, and aversion. According to Buddhist thought, the wisdom deficit or ignorance that arises from being attached to an inherently existing self is the underlying cause of all forms of suffering, including the entire spectrum of psychological disorders. The ultimate goal is thus the unwavering understanding of impermanence of self. This goal likely deviates from the aim of most individuals seeking MBIs within medical, psychological, or clinical settings (Shonin, Van Gordon, & Griffiths, 2013).

A second distinction between Eastern and Western views concerns the intended beneficiaries of the practices of mindfulness. Western psychological treatments, including MBIs, are historically steeped in ego strengthening, and generally aim to reduce suffering within the individual. The Buddhist perspective, however, offers a vision of radical inter-identification: a philosophy in which all living beings are identified with all other living begins. As a reflection of this interdependence (*pratityasamutpada*), the Buddhist practice aims to eliminate the root cause of suffering for *all sentient beings*, not just the specific individual practicing mindfulness. While many Western MBIs now focus on compassion of self and others, the compassion generally has a specific object or recipient, often called referential compassion. Alternatively, Buddhist training facilitates the development of nonreferential, or unbiased, compassion: universal compassion for all sentient beings (Halifax, 2011; Rosch, 2003).

A third and related aspect of the Buddhist conceptualization of mindfulness that, until recently, has been absent in Western literature includes the development of the *Four Immeasurables*: loving kindness (*metta*), compassion (*karuna*), empathic joy (mudita), and equanimity (*upekkha*). Loving kindness is defined as the wish for all sentient beings to have happiness and its causes (Salzberg, 2011). Compassion is defined as the wish for all sentient beings to be free from suffering and its causes. Empathic joy is the celebrating and finding joy in the happiness and success of others. Equanimity has been defined as an even minded mental state that cannot be swayed by biases or preferences (Bodhi, 2005; Desbordes et al., 2014). These four deeply interrelated immeasurable attitudes are often generated and then directed toward all other sentient beings. The development of the Four Immeasurables is thought to be necessary to foster the wisdom of interdependence, and in-turn, the wisdom of interdependence facilitates the development of compassion and loving kindness for others (Rosch, 2003).

A fourth, and perhaps most controversial, feature of the Buddhist conceptualization that is frequently lacking in Westerns models is the lack of explicit ethical teachings (Baer, 2003; Christopher, Woodrich, & Tiernan, 2014; Grossman, 2015; Lindahl, 2015; Van Gordon, Shonin, Griffiths, & Singh, 2014). Ethics play a large role in every Buddhist tradition and are an essential foundation of a mindfulness practice. Right Mindfulness is informed and developed in conjunction with the prior path factors of the Eight Noble Path, most of which require the exercise of mental restraint and behavioral ethical disciplines (*sīla*). Right View acts as an ethical compass for the other seven interdependent factors (Right Thought, Right Speech, Right Livelihood, Right Effort, Right Mindfulness, and Right Concentration). The term *Right* can also be interpreted as skillful, and signifies that each element of the path leads to reduced suffering for self or others. For example, Right Livelihood means earning one's living in a way that is benevolent and causes no harm to self or others. Ethical behavior in Buddhist traditions is further described in the Five Precepts: refrain from killing, stealing, lying, sexual misconduct, and misuse of intoxicants. This ethical foundation establishes a motivation and desire for liberation and freedom, provides a framework for viewing experiences in terms of the continuation of suffering, and discerns appropriate and wholesome behaviors in light of this framework of suffering (Dhargyey, 1974; Purser & Milillo, 2015).

This formula suggests that mindfulness is not merely a cataloged tool for enhancing attention. Instead, it is informed and influenced by many other factors: view of reality; the nature of thoughts, speech, and actions; methods of earning a living; and effort in avoiding unwholesome and unskillful states while developing those that are skillful and favorable to health, contentment, and wisdom. These ethical guidelines are an intractable aspect of the Buddhist

Loving kindness, one of the Four Immeasurables, is often included in mindfulness-based interventions

path of personal transformation, and are understood not as commandments from a higher authority, but as pragmatic ways of facilitating one's own awakening and the well-being of others.

According to some authors, the absence of explicitly taught ethics in secular MBIs is a source of concern because it could lead to the development of wrong mindfulness, or mindfulness used for harmful purposes (Monteiro, Musten, & Compson, 2015). Codes of professional ethics, however, require respect for cultural diversity and self-determination and make it problematic for mental health and other professionals to teach ethics based on a particular religious or spiritual framework in many contemporary secular settings. Personal values and cross-cultural virtues have stronger theoretical and empirical foundations in psychological science, can be used in a variety of secular settings, and are appropriate for a wide range of clients, regardless of their religious or spiritual orientations (Baer, 2015).

Operational definitions of mindfulness differ among Western and Buddhist conceptualizations

A final discrepancy between Buddhist and Western conceptualizations concerns the ability to assess or measure mindfulness. While Western science suggests that the construct of mindfulness must be operationally defined and operationalized to be accurately assessed and quantified, most Eastern traditions dictate that mindfulness cannot be easily extracted and analyzed from inter-related constructs (Christopher et al., 2009; Grossman, 2011). Furthermore, Buddhist texts primarily refer to mindfulness not as a mental function or trait but as a practice or process (Anālayo, 2004; Bodhi, 2011). Recently, a group of Zen Buddhist clergy and practitioners were asked to assess the validity of measures of Western mindfulness, and several concerns emerged. Participants noted that levels and duration of practice could influence the interpretation of the items, leading individuals who may be more mindful to rate themselves with less mindfulness. Another concern was that the measures were lacking in their ability to assess the nonlinear and evolutionary aspect of the practice. A final concern was that the measures appeared to be assessing noncritical aspects of mindfulness, while lacking essential elements of a mindful practice, such as one's awareness of aversion and suffering and the intention to return awareness to the present moment (Christopher, Woodrich, & Tiernan, 2014).

Western and Eastern perspectives on mindfulness overlap, yet there are several clear differences between them

The contribution of the Buddhist tradition has been an exceptional influence to Western science and this cultural phenomenon is likely still in its infancy. Current Western MBIs and Buddhist teachings share the overarching intention to alleviate suffering, as well as the understanding that behavioral, cognitive, affective, and biological experiences can be influenced through the practice of mental training. Despite these foundational shared views, there are clear differences. Understanding the origins of mindfulness, the historical context of Buddhism from which mindfulness arose, the shared commonalities, and the important differences between these conceptualizations, may be helpful and important for effective intervention implementation and future theoretical development.

2

Theories and Models

2.1   The "Mindfulness-Based" Movement

2.1.1   Mindfulness-Based Stress Reduction (MBSR)

Application of mindfulness meditation as a Western, secularized intervention approach began largely with the work of Jon Kabat-Zinn in the late 1980s. Kabat-Zinn explored the use of mindfulness meditation in treating patients with chronic pain, a program now known as mindfulness-based stress reduction (MBSR; Kabat-Zinn et al., 1985). MBSR is theoretically grounded in secularized Buddhist meditation practices, mind-body medicine, and the transactional model of stress, which suggests that people can be taught to manage stress by adjusting their cognitive perspective and increasing their coping skills. The primary aims of MBSR are to enhance attentional control and receptive awareness by focusing on internal (bodily sensations, breath, thoughts, emotions) and external (sights, sounds) stimuli in the present moment. With this enhanced attentional allocation and awareness, it is postulated that one may skillfully, rather than habitually or reactively, respond to the present moment experience. This process allows for a larger, and potentially more skillful, behavioral repertoire in the presence of stress and adversity.

> MBSR has provided a foundation for the development of numerous other secular mindfulness-based interventions

A typical MBSR course is delivered in a group format and consists of eight weekly 2.5-hour sessions and an all-day (6-hour) retreat session. In addition, regular home meditation practice, for about 45 minutes daily, is expected. MBSR groups are frequently transdiagnostic in nature, emphasizing that all participants, regardless of disorder, experience an ongoing stream of constantly changing internal states and have the ability to cultivate moment-to-moment awareness.

MBSR sessions are largely experiential with considerable time dedicated to mindfulness practice. The *raisin exercise* is the first experimental activity. Participants are invited to see, feel, smell, and taste an individual raisin with an elevated sense of curiosity and interest. This primary exercise is intended to experientially discern mindful awareness from *automatic pilot,* the tendency to act with limited awareness of one's thoughts, emotions, or behaviors. The discussion following this practice typically centers on the direct sensory experiences of the raisin, the mind's tendencies to wander or judge, and the nature of automatic pilot. The MBSR facilitator discusses with participants how automatic pilot can be advantageous at times; however, these unconscious thoughts, feelings, and physical sensations can also trigger habits of thinking and behaving that are harmful and can lead to greater stress and worsening mood. Cultivating mindfulness while engaging in seemingly mundane daily activities, such as eating or washing dishes, is encouraged throughout the eight weeks to enhance awareness and promote the understanding of the inter-relationships between habitual thought, emotion, and behavior. Participants are also asked to notice pleasant and unpleasant events and the associated thoughts, emotions, and sensations. This practice cultivates increased aware-ness and appreciation of pleasant events when they occur, and recognition of the associated sensations and emotions. This may also help participants explore the tendency to catalog experiences as pleasant or unpleasant, and to attempt to cling to pleasant experiences and avoid or get rid of unpleasant ones.

Throughout the course, an assortment of mindfulness practices are intro-duced, including the body scan, mindful breathing, mindful movement, and walking meditation. During the body scan, also introduced in the first session, attention is directed sequentially throughout the body in order to cultivate a nonjudgmental awareness of physical sensations, cognitions, and emotions. This is based on the understanding of the body as the first foundation, or first object, of mindfulness, as taught in the *Satipaṭṭhāna* and *Mahāsatipaṭṭhāna Suttas*. Participants cultivate the ability to *sense* or *perceive* the bodily sen-sations, without referring to the narratives and judgments about the body. By tuning into the body on its own terms, the direct experience of the body breathing, its movements, postures, anatomical parts, the elements of which it is composed, as well as its impermanence, participants gain practice in refer-ring to experience itself, rather than the secondary appraisal of experience (Anālayo, 2004). Therefore, during the body scan, sensations in each area are carefully observed; participants are encouraged to simply perceive rather than think about or evaluate sensation. As the mind becomes distracted, attention is gently returned to the sensations arising and passing in the current moment. In the practice of mindfulness of breath, attention is similarly directed to physical sensations in the body. In this practice, however, the chosen target of attention is the sensations that arise in the body as breathing occurs. The intention differs from *breathing exercises* or deep breathing in that participants are instructed not to attempt to change or control breathing, but to allow the body to breathe naturally, and to bring attention to the associated sensations. When the mind wanders from the breath, the participant notices this shift, and perhaps the con-tent of the distraction, and focus is gently returned to the sensations of breath-ing. Mindful movement cultivates an individual's awareness of the bodily sensations while slowly and gently moving, stretching, or holding a position. Similarly, during walking meditation, attention is deliberately focused on the sensations in the body while walking, including the shifting of weight and balance and sensations in one's legs and feet. Finally, open-focused practice invites the individual to expand his or her attention to include sounds in the environment, sounds and sensations of breathing, bodily sensations, and the stream of constantly changing thoughts and emotions with a curious, nonreac-tive, and nonjudgmental stance. All these practices aim to develop concentra-tion, attentional flexibility, and interoceptive awareness. Furthermore, during these practices, one begins to notice the transitory nature of experience, as well as the frequency and automaticity of judgmental and narrative thinking.

During each session, the teacher facilitates discussions that explore partici-pants' experiences with in-session and home practices. Rather than providing advice or behavioral change strategies, discussions employ mindful inquiry and focus on detailed explorations of participants' experiences of mindfulness, whether positive, negative, or neutral, while modeling a curious, non-judgmental, and accepting stance toward whatever is being shared. Poetry and metaphors are frequently used to model the processes of mindfulness. Psychoeducation regarding the science of mindfulness and tools to integrate mindfulness into daily living are also provided.

2.1.2   Mindfulness-Based Cognitive Therapy (MBCT)

Developed in 2002 by Segal, Williams, and Teasdale, MBCT integrates cognitive behavioral therapy (CBT) and MBSR approaches and practices. Grounded in a cognitive model that identifies contributing factors to the vulnerability of relapse, MBCT was developed for individuals with a history of major depression who were currently in remission, to reduce the likelihood of relapse without relying on extended use of medication. According to MBCT, ordinary sad moods may be more likely to reactivate depressive thought content and a ruminative style of thinking among previously depressed individuals. Negative rumination and depressive thought content, compounded with a tendency for behavioral avoidance, is thought to increase the likelihood of another major depressive episode (Segal, Williams, Teasdale, & Gemar, 1996).

MBCT was developed to prevent the recurrence of episodes of depression among individuals currently in remission

MBCT teaches practices that foster acceptance and decentering as alternatives to experiential avoidance and rumination. Acceptance in this context can be described as a willingness to fully experience the present moment without defense, making space for all aspects of one's internal landscape: pleasant, unpleasant, and neutral. *Decentering*, defined as the ability to view thoughts and emotions as impermanent and to tolerate aversive experience without engaging in rigid avoidance (Teasdale et al., 2002), involves a nonjudgmental, nonreactive awareness of one's cognitions, emotions, and sensations as they occur. This approach to the present moment can slow reactivity to mood, increase psychological flexibility, and provide the freedom to choose a new response to habitual stimuli. These shifts in relationship to one's experiences can reduce the likelihood that mood or negative thoughts will escalate into a major depressive episode.

MBCT is typically conducted as an 8-week group with 2-hour sessions, often with no more than 12 group members. MBCT employs many of the same activities used in MBSR: The raisin exercise, body scans, breath meditation, mindful movement, mindful walking, mindfulness during daily activities, and monitoring of pleasant and unpleasant events. Also similar to MBSR, poetry and metaphors are used to support the attitudes and concepts underlying this approach. The importance of homework and the nature of mindful inquiry are also applicable to MBCT. Didactic information and CBT content in MBCT focuses primarily on the nature of depression rather than on stress.

While there are many similarities to MBSR, several exercises and practices were developed specifically for MBCT. The Three-Minute Breathing Space, for example, is described as a three step, mini-meditation encouraged to be practiced throughout the day, with a focus on use during challenging experiences, or in the event of potential triggers for depressogenic thinking. The

Three-Minute Breathing Space provides a specific practice for stepping out of the "automatic" tendencies towards ruminative or reactive cognitive patterns, and to establish a clearer awareness of the present moment. Step one of the practice is labeled *Awareness*, and involves cultivating a nonreactive awareness of internal experiences (thoughts, emotions, and physical sensations). Step two is labeled *Focus*, and involves focusing attention and attending to the sensations of breathing. Step three is labeled *Expand*. In this final step, the participant expands awareness to include breathing, bodily sensations, posture, facial expression, as well as thoughts and emotions, with a nonjudgmental and nonreactive stance. MBCT also integrates several exercises from cognitive therapy that emphasize a decentered approach to internal experiences. The Thoughts and Emotions exercise aims to illustrate thought-emotion chaining in which a situation leads to a thought or interpretation, which then leads to a feeling or emotional response. A discussion of automatic thoughts related to depression helps participants learn to recognize the types of thoughts that are typical of depression, and to understand them as symptoms of depression rather than as true statements about themselves or reality. Pleasure and mastery activities are generated as behavioral activation strategies to help participants come into contact with naturally reinforcing experiences. In the final two sessions, participants develop relapse prevention action plans, in which they are encouraged to make lists of their individual *relapse signatures* that indicate a depressive episode might be developing. Participants generate action plans that incorporate the skills taught in the preceding sessions to use when they notice these signs.

2.1.3   Mindfulness-Based Relapse Prevention (MBRP)

MBRP is based on different mindfulness approaches and CBT relapse prevention for addictive disorders

MBRP (Bowen et al., 2011) is an outpatient aftercare treatment approach for individuals with substance use disorders who have completed initial inpatient or intensive outpatient treatment. As with MBSR and MBCT, formal mindfulness training is central to MBRP, supplemented with cognitive-behavioral relapse prevention treatment components, such as self-monitoring and relapse chain analyses (Marlatt & Gordon, 1985). The structure of the program also mirrors that of MBSR and MBCT, typically delivered in a closed group-format over eight weeks and involving eight sequential 2-hour weekly sessions. MBRP is designed to target three factors that play a key role in returning to problematic substance use following treatment: (1) lack of awareness of various internal (thoughts, physical sensations, emotions) and external (environmental factors) aspects of the present moment; (2) reactivity to aversive internal or external experiences, and perceived lack of ability to withstand aversion without reacting; and (3) lack of kindness and compassion towards oneself and one's experience, or a sense of shame and self-blame. To address these three factors, MBRP employs many of the same activities used in MBSR and MBCT, such as the raisin exercise, body scan, breath meditation, mindful movement, mindful walking, mindfulness during daily activities, and monitoring of pleasant and unpleasant daily activities. The importance of homework, and the nature of mindful inquiry, as discussed in the MBSR section, also apply to MBRP.

In addition to the MBSR practices, the "SOBER breathing space" in MBRP was adapted from MBCT's Three-Minute Breathing Space, and it is a central practice in MBRP. The SOBER breathing space is a *mini-meditation*, or informal mindfulness practice, designed to facilitate the flexible use of mindfulness skills in everyday life and during high-risk situations that may precipitate relapse. SOBER is an acronym designed to help participants remember the steps of this practice: *Stop, Observe, Breath focus, Expand, and Respond.* MBRP participants are instructed to practice the SOBER throughout the day to *check-in* with their experience, and to use the practice in challenging or high-risk situations to help respond skillfully in events that may typically be triggering. Another core practice in MBRP is the *urge surfing* practice, which is fundamentally an exposure and response prevention exercise designed to enhance tolerance of and reduce reactivity to substance cravings or other behavioral urges. The practice is taught by leading participants through an imaginal exposure to a high-risk situation, perhaps beginning with a minimally distressing experience, and guiding them to stay present with, and bring an open and curious attention to, the direct experience of this urge or reactivity, without engaging in reactive or avoidant behavior. Participants are taught to attend to the elemental aspects of physical sensation, thoughts, and emotions that arise, and to investigate what their underlying need might be in this situation. This practice is introduced in the second session, and participants are encouraged to continue to bring this same curious examination to challenging encounters throughout the remaining weeks of the course.

MBRP also aims to promote self-compassion and nonjudgment towards oneself and one's experience. The loving kindness, or *metta*, meditation is intended to explore and enhance kindness towards oneself and others. As in other mindfulness-based programs, MBRP also uses metaphors to help participants come in contact with skillful qualities or understandings. For example, the mountain meditation, based on a practice in MBSR, is intended to help participants cultivate and bring awareness to his or her inner resources (e.g., stability, dignity and equanimity in the face of potentially triggering phenomena).

Other mindfulness-based approaches for substance use disorders have been adapted from MBSR and/or MBRP (Amaro, Spear, Vallejo, Conron, & Black, 2014; Brewer et al., 2011; Zgierska et al., 2008) or developed independently (e.g., mindfulness-oriented recovery enhancement; Garland, Roberts-Lewis, Tronnier, Graves, & Kelley, 2015). Reviews of the efficacy of alternative interventions may be a useful resource for practitioners considering MBIs for substance use disorders (Witkiewitz, Bowen, et al., 2014; Zgierska et al., 2009).

2.1.4 Other Mindfulness-Based Approaches Based on the MBSR Model

Several other MBIs tailored to specific populations continue to be developed, assessed, and implemented with promising results, including interventions specifically for children (Lee, Semple, Rosa, & Miller, 2008), adolescents (Zylowska et al., 2008), first responders (Christopher et al., 2015), and physicians, medical students, and healthcare providers (Krasner et al., 2009). Here we focus on reviewing three recently developed interventions: Mindfulness-

Based Cancer Recovery (MBCR; Carlson & Speca, 2011), Mindfulness-Based Eating Awareness Training (MB-EAT) for binge eating disorder (Kristeller, Wolever, & Sheets, 2013), and Mindfulness-Based Therapy for Insomnia (MBTI; Ong et al., 2014).

MBCR (Carlson & Speca, 2011) is an adaption of MBSR developed to more effectively address the challenges faced by individuals diagnosed with cancer. MBCR has a unique emphasis on how mindfulness training can assist individuals in reflecting on identity and search for meaning during a personal experience with cancer. Additionally, MBCR focuses on how intentionally cultivating present-focused awareness may be helpful for patients who are often overwhelmed with regrets about the past, and fear and uncertainty about the future.

MB-EAT (Kristeller & Wolever, 2011; Kristeller et al., 2013) was developed as a treatment for binge eating disorder. A central focus of MB-EAT is cultivating awareness of one's eating experience and one's behavior in relation to food. Specifically, participants engage in a variety of mindful eating practices and homework assignments designed to enhance awareness of internal hunger and satiety cues, ability to savor the food experience, and ability to recognize mindless eating and make conscious food choices. MB-EAT also involves practices aimed at reducing negative affective reactions to both emotional triggers and self-judgment about binge eating. Participants learn to identify and tolerate challenging emotional triggers, and to practice openness to and acceptance of themselves and their bodies as they are. Finally, throughout the MB-EAT program, clients are encouraged to draw upon both their *inner wisdom* (e.g., awareness of internal experiences) and *outer wisdom* (e.g., general knowledge and standard guidelines about healthy eating) when making decisions about food-related behaviors in their day-to-day lives.

MBTI (Ong et al., 2014) integrates components of MBSR (e.g., sitting meditations, mindful yoga) with behavioral strategies for insomnia (e.g., stimulus control, sleep hygiene, and sleep restriction techniques). A core aim of MBTI is to help participants shift their relationship with thoughts and beliefs about sleep in order to reduce secondary arousal, mitigating the cycle of insomnia (Ong, Ulmer, & Manber, 2012). Through a variety of mindfulness practices, participants learn to adopt a more balanced, flexible, and nonattached stance towards sleep-related thoughts that occur both during the day and at night.

2.2   Related Models and Approaches

We have reviewed a few of the many contemporary interventions for mental health disorders and medical conditions that integrate mindfulness practices, including MBSR, MBCT, MBRP, MB-EAT, MBCR, and MBTI. We have focused thus far on those that are part of the newly-emerging MBIs with both formal and informal practice included in each treatment session, as well as assigned between sessions. MBIs are unique treatment protocols in that a central aim is to foster regular (daily, if possible) meditation practice as the primary training to shift participants' views, approaches and reactions to both *mundane* and triggering situations of daily life. Other cognitive- and/or behaviorally-based interventions, such as dialectical behavior therapy (DBT; Linehan, 1993a, 1993b), metacognitive therapy (MCT; Wells, 2000), compassion focused therapy (CFT; Gilbert, 2009), and acceptance and commitment therapy (ACT; Hayes, Strosahl, & Wilson, 2013), also draw upon mindfulness principles and involve mindfulness training. Where these differ, however, is in the centrality of formal mindfulness meditation practice. In these latter mentioned approaches, mindfulness is often practiced in the form of brief exercises, or *informally*, and mindfulness is one of several treatment components rather than the primary foundation of the training. This differentiation is not to argue for or against either approach, nor to pit them against one another, but to illuminate what is an understandable confusion to those learning about these difference therapeutic programs. This is likely due in part to the broad semantic meaning of the word *mindfulness*, as this term does not differentiate between diverse approaches, such as exercises or metaphors intended to raise awareness or compassion, versus formal mindfulness meditation practice. Below, we briefly review the forms and functions of mindfulness-informed theories and practices in the context of dialectical behavior therapy, metacognitive therapy, compassion focused therapy and acceptance and commitment therapy.

> Numerous recent psychological interventions draw upon mindfulness principles and practices

2.2.1 Dialectical Behavior Therapy

DBT (Linehan, 1993a) was originally developed as a psychosocial treatment for borderline personality disorder (BPD). According to the biopsychosocial theory of BPD, emotion dysregulation is its core feature (Linehan, 1993a, 1993b). This is characterized by emotional vulnerability (e.g., sensitivity to emotional cues), inability to label and tolerate emotional distress, and impulsive and problematic behavioral responses to emotions that perpetuate emotional suffering. In DBT, mindfulness skills are viewed as critical in helping an individual with BPD develop more adaptive responses to emotion-related situations and emotional experiences. These skills, often divided into categories of *what* and *how*, are core components of DBT skills training. The *what* skills include observing what is happening in the moment, describing one's experience with words, and fully participating or engaging in whatever activity one is doing. The *how* skills include bringing a nonjudgmental stance to one's experience, focusing on one thing at a time, and responding to situations with the ultimate goal of *doing what works* rather than doing what is *right*. These skills are taught through a variety of means including didactic handouts, the use of metaphors, mindfulness exercises (e.g., breath meditation), and feedback and coaching.

2.2.2 Metacognitive Therapy

MCT emerged from the self-regulatory information processing theory of emotional disorder (Wells & Matthews, 1996). MCT is viewed as a transdiagnostic approach and proposes that the maintenance of all psychopathology is linked to a perseverative thinking style called the cognitive attentional syndrome. This cognitive pattern consists of inflexible, self-focused attention, perseverative thinking styles (worry/rumination), attentional strategies of threat monitoring, and maladaptive coping and self-regulatory behaviors such as avoidance and thought suppression (Wells, 2000). MCT focuses on how one manages, observes, and processes thoughts, and aims to address feedback loops among metacognitive beliefs, thought control techniques, and environmental stressors that perpetuate and exacerbate psychopathology and disrupted social functioning.

MCT is stand-alone treatment conducted either in individual or group format. MCT consist of several techniques designed to reduce an individual's vulnerability to dysfunctional self-referent processing, three of which are attention training, detached mindfulness, and behavioral experiments targeting metacognitions (Bennett & Wells, 2010; Wells, 2000). Attention training (Wells, 2005) is an auditory task which consist of focusing attention onto external auditory information, intended to promote attentional control and detachment from self-referent thoughts. Detached mindfulness consists of meta-awareness (consciousness of thoughts), cognitive de-centering (comprehension of thoughts as events versus facts), attentional detachment (attention is flexible and not anchored to any one event), low conceptual processing (low levels of analytical and meaning based appraisals. i.e., inner dialogue), and low goal-directed coping (goals to remove or avoid threat are not paramount). Finally, behavioral experiments are used to test the validity of metacognitive beliefs.

2.2.3 Compassion Focused Therapy

CFT is a transdiagnostic approach for people with high shame and self-criticism whose problems tend to be chronic (Gilbert, 2009). An integrated and multimodal behavioral treatment, CFT is based on research from attachment theory, Buddhist psychology, and the neuroscience of affiliation. CFT was explicitly designed to address shame and self-criticism (Gilbert, 2010; Gilbert & Procter, 2006). CFT postulates that individuals prone to high levels of shame and self-criticism find it difficult to generate feelings of contentment, safety, or warmth in their relationships with others and themselves. CFT uses compassion training to target both self-criticism and shame and increase capacities for experiencing affiliative emotions, especially self-generated experiences of inner warmth, safety, and soothing.

CFT is often delivered within individual therapy, but is also suited for group format (Judge, Cleghorn, McEwan, & Gilbert, 2012), and typically ranges from 3 to 12 weeks. In sessions, psychoeducation of the evolutionary model is provided to depersonalize and de-shame difficulties by assisting people in understanding that many cognitive biases/distortions are built-in biological processes, constructed by genetics and the environment (Gilbert, 2009). CFT defines compassion as "a sensitivity to suffering in self and others, with a commitment to try to alleviate and prevent it," and is understood in terms of specific attributes and skills (Gilbert, 2009). Attributes include self-care, sensitivity and awareness to emotions and personal needs, distress tolerance, empathy, and nonjudgmental awareness. These attributes are demonstrated by the therapist who helps participants develop an internal, compassionate relationship with themselves as an alternative to the blaming, shaming, and condemning internal tone. Key techniques and skills involved in CFT sessions include the use of imagery, soothing rhythm breathing, compassionate thinking directed towards self and others, responding to self-criticism through self-compassion, and practicing compassionate behavior. These techniques are often complimented with letter or diary writing. CFT has a strong focus on nurturing compassion within the self, and encourages the client to focus on, understand, and feel compassion to the self during negative thought processes (Tirch & Gilbert, 2015).

Noncontrolled studies have found significant improvements using CFT for people with psychotic and complex disorders (Braehler et al., 2013; Gumley, Braehler, Laithwaite, MacBeth, & Gilbert, 2010), personality disorders (Lucre & Corten, 2013), eating disorders (Gale, Gilbert, Read, & Goss, 2014), and heterogeneous mental health problems in people presenting to community mental health teams (Judge et al., 2012). CFT has been found to be a helpful addition and focus for people with acquired brain injury (Ashworth, Gracey, & Gilbert, 2011). Findings from a recent meta-analysis that included 14 studies, containing three RCTs, suggested that CFT shows promise as an intervention for mood disorders, particularly for those patients high in self-criticism; however, more large-scale, high-quality trials are needed before it can be considered evidence-based practice (Leaviss & Uttley, 2015).

Preliminary research on CFT shows promise, yet further research is needed comparing it to other interventions

2.2.4 Acceptance and Commitment Therapy

ACT (Hayes et al., 2013) is a transdiagnostic behavior therapy approach that has been applied to a range of mental health disorders and medical conditions, including depression, anxiety disorders, chronic pain, psychosis, and substance use disorders (Hayes, Luoma, Bond, Masuda, & Lillis, 2006). ACT interventions are based on six core processes believed to be fundamental to both psychopathology and psychological health. Principles of mindfulness and acceptance are central to this model, with four out of the six processes being mindfulness- and acceptance-based. These include: (1) *being present*, the ability to bring a flexible attention to present moment experience, (2) *defusion*, the ability to *step back* and observe private events rather than automatically believing or attaching oneself to private events, (3) *experiential acceptance*, an openness and willingness to experience difficult private events without undue efforts to escape or avoid one's experience, and (4) *self-as-context*, the ability to connect with a sense of an observer self that is a constant and stable observer of ever-changing experiences. The other two processes in ACT model center on behavioral commitment to values: (1) *values clarity*, a clear awareness of personally chosen values and life directions, and (2) *committed action*, the ability to engage in sustained patterns of behavior that are linked to values. The purpose of all ACT interventions is to target these processes in order to promote psychological flexibility, or the overall ability to bring an open, flexible, and present-focused awareness to the full range of one's experience in life, and to make conscious choices that are in the service of one's values.

ACT interventions employ a variety of methods to target the six core processes noted above. These methods include the use of metaphor, mindfulness exercises, exposure techniques, functional analysis, values clarification exercises, and behavioral activation techniques. As noted, mindfulness training is one method used in ACT to train mindfulness and acceptance processes, but it is certainly not the only method. Compared to MBIs, such as MBSR, practicing formal mindfulness meditation outside of therapy sessions is not emphasized to the same degree in ACT. Another unique aspect of ACT, as compared to the MBIs, is its explicit focus on values. The MBIs discussed previously may acknowledge the importance of values and integrate discussion of values throughout the intervention. However, the ACT model explicitly focuses on commitment to values as a core element of psychological health and valued living as the ultimate outcome of treatment.

2.3   Mechanisms of Action

Researchers are beginning to investigate processes or mechanisms that illuminate how and why mindfulness promotes well-being

Along with the rapid development of various MBIs, researchers are increasingly interested in understanding *how* mindfulness, as a state, a trait, a practice, and an intervention, promotes psychological and physical health. To date, researchers have proposed numerous theories of mechanisms of change facilitated by mindfulness, and here we review the most prominent mechanisms described in the recent literature, from both cross-sectional studies and longitudinal intervention trials in varied populations.

2.3.1   Reductions in Maladaptive Self-Regulation and Experiential Avoidance

Chiesa, Anselmi, and Serretti (2014) suggested mindfulness may be linked to positive health outcomes in part because it reduces maladaptive self-regulation such as avoidant coping, experiential avoidance, and rumination. Avoidant coping and experiential avoidance are similar constructs; avoidant coping is defined as behaviors (e.g., distraction, denial, drug use) aimed at avoiding a stressful event or reducing thoughts and emotions associated with the event (Carver, Scheier, & Weintraub, 1989), and experiential avoidance is defined as an overall trait-like tendency to overly engage in behaviors that function to modify the form, frequency, or duration of undesired private events and situations that elicit them (Hayes et al., 2013). According to the theoretical model underlying ACT, for example, experiential avoidance is a core feature across most forms of psychopathology, and the ability to bring a flexible and present-focused attention to one's experience is essential in reducing experiential avoidance (Hayes et al., 2013). Research has shown that both avoidant coping and experiential avoidance consistently predict poor mental health outcomes (Chawla & Ostafin, 2007; Karekla & Panayiotou, 2011). Rumination, or excessive and repetitive thinking about the causes and consequences of a problem, has also been shown to be consistently related to poor mental health outcomes (Nolen-Hoeksema, Wisco, & Lyubomirsky, 2008). Hence, mindfulness may exert salutary effects by helping individuals learn to stay with, rather than attempt to escape or avoid, aversive experiences, and to refrain from engaging in extreme cognitive elaboration about these experiences. A recent meta-analytic study on the mechanisms of mindfulness found moderately strong and consistent evidence that reduction in rumination is a mechanism of change in MBSR and MBCT (Gu, Strauss, Bond, & Cavanagh, 2015).

Decreases in self-reported rumination may be one mechanism through which MBSR and MBCT exert their therapeutic effects

2.3.2 Emotion Regulation

Emotional regulation is the process of modulating the occurrence of emotions, as well as one's experience and expression of emotions (Gross, 2015). Several mindfulness researchers have posited that increases in adaptive emotion regulation abilities may be a mechanism of mindfulness (Chiesa et al., 2014; Roemer, Williston, & Rollins, 2015). Roemer et al. (2015) recently reviewed theoretical and empirical studies that have examined the relationship between mindfulness and emotion regulation. They concluded that correlational and experimental studies have consistently demonstrated a positive association between mindfulness practice and adaptive emotion regulation, and that there is good preliminary evidence that MBIs enhance emotion regulation abilities. Roemer et al. (2015) also outlined several reasons proposed by various researchers as to why mindfulness facilitates adaptive emotion regulation: (1) enhanced inhibitory learning through exposure to negative emotions without engagement in avoidant behaviors, (2) enhanced sensitivity to internal and external cues that signal the need to regulate emotions, (3) enhanced awareness of early emotional arousal (e.g., body sensations) that facilitates the ability to regulate emotions at an earlier point in the emotional activation process, (4) enhanced ability to reappraise or reevaluate the meaning of emotional experiences themselves and stressful environmental events, and (5) enhanced ability to dispassionately observe and label emotions as they occur, which may in turn directly change trajectories of emotional responses or may indirectly affect emotions by enhancing one's ability to tolerate emotions without engaging in reflexive responses (e.g., suppression, rumination, drug use) that may ultimately intensify negative emotions.

Vago and Silbersweig (2012) focused on changes in automatic emotion regulation as one key process affected by the cultivation of mindfulness. They distinguished automatic emotion regulation, which occurs at a nonconscious level, from conscious emotion regulation, which involves intentional cognitive processes or behaviors aimed at regulating emotions. According to Vago and Silbersweig (2012), mindfulness practice can directly affect automatic emotional reactivity to stressors (sympathetic nervous system) and automatic homeostatic mechanisms in response to stressors (parasympathetic nervous systems). For example, mindfulness practice may decrease initial emotional reactivity to stressors and may enhance mechanisms that allow an individual to recover from emotional arousal and return to a baseline state. To support their theory, Vago and Silbersweig (2012) reviewed numerous studies showing that experienced meditators appear to exhibit improved automatic emotion regulation as compared to nonmeditators.

Mindfulness practice may influence both conscious and automatic emotion regulation processes

2.3.3   Values-Consistent Behavior

Brown and Ryan (2003) posited that mindfulness can enhance one's overall ability to make autonomous choices that are in line with one's values. They suggested that mindfulness might increase one's awareness of ongoing internal and external cues that are related to one's values, thereby making it more likely that an individual will behave in a manner that is in accordance with valued goals.

Several researchers have posited that mindfulness enhances values clarity and values-based behavior

Other researchers have also focused on the role of values in their discussion of mindfulness. For instance, consistent with the conceptualization of Brown and Ryan (2003) of how mindfulness enhances well-being, from an ACT perspective, mindfulness is essential for facilitating values-consistent behavior (Hayes et al., 2013). Additionally, the model of Shapiro et al. (2006) of mindfulness suggests that values clarification may be a key mechanism that explains the benefits of mindfulness. Their model emphasizes that mindfulness may allow an individual to consciously reflect on his or her values and freely choose valued directions rather than reflexively adopting values imposed by others.

2.3.4   Regulatory Flexibility

Mindfulness increases one's ability to flexibly respond to fluctuating demands in one's situational context

Some researchers have focused on how mindfulness may promote well-being by facilitating *flexible* self-regulatory responses to events. Shapiro and colleagues (2006) posited that flexibility is a key mechanism of mindfulness, emphasizing that mindfulness may allow one to flexibly regulate behavior based on what is actually occurring in the environment rather than reacting rigidly and reflexively in ways that are not responsive to changes in the environment. Similarly, Brown, Ryan, & Creswell (2007) suggested that mindfulness enhances one's ability to engage in flexible responses to events. According to the psychological flexibility model in ACT, mindfulness abilities are essential in allowing one to make conscious contact with one's present moment experience, including those experiences that are difficult or distressing, allowing an individual greater flexibility in choosing behaviors that serve personally chosen valued goals (Hayes et al., 2013).

Although the broad construct of regulatory flexibility has been defined in several ways (Aldao & Gross, 2015; Bonanno & Burton, 2013; Cheng & Chan, 2014; Kashdan & Rottenberg, 2010; Kato, 2012), there is growing consensus that regulatory flexibility may involve: (1) the ability to accurately perceive and discriminate among contextual features in order to select a regulatory strategy that provides the best match to a situation, (2) the ability to draw upon a wide range of regulatory strategies within one's repertoire, and (3) the ability to adjust one's behavioral responses in accordance with new information about a situation. Further research is needed to clarify how mindfulness is related to each of these components of flexibility and the degree to which these components may explain the link between mindfulness and positive health outcomes.

3

Assessment and Treatment Indications

3.1   Indications

As can be seen in Section 2.3, the mechanisms of action that have been attributed to mindfulness are indicative of mindfulness as a transdiagnostic approach suitable for numerous psychological disorders. Maladaptive self-regulation, experiential avoidance, poor emotional regulation, and inconsistent values behavior are problems found in addiction, depression, anxiety, borderline personality disorder, psychosis, eating disorders, and some physical health problems. Mindfulness training has also been identified as a useful tool for improving mental and physical health among people who do not meet criteria for a psychological disorder.

3.2   Different Forms of Mindfulness

The term mindfulness has a multitude of different meanings, especially as used and understood in contemporary Western contexts. Each of these definitions, or conceptualizations, may call for a different form of assessment. As such, operationalizing *mindfulness* remains elusive. Thus, a gold standard assessment that characterizes all of the multiple uses, characteristics, and qualities of mindfulness has yet to be developed. In this section, we review some of the current challenges of assessing mindfulness, and provide an overview of extant contemporary assessment approaches that have been developed to best characterize and measure mindfulness.

3.2.1   Mindfulness as a Practice

As reflected in contemporary literature and debates, there are multiple ways of conceptualizing, describing, practicing, or understanding mindfulness. First, mindfulness can be understood as a practice. In the context of medical and psychological treatment, we are trying to engage our participants in these programs in the practice of mindfulness. In many meditation traditions, both the students and teachers of mindfulness meditation are referred to as "practitioners," and the engagement itself is referred to as "practice." This is a clear reflection of the understanding that this is a way of seeing and interacting with oneself and the interrelated environment that is, by its nature, an ongoing practice versus a skill that is mastered. Thus, it presents challenging issues to our

One way to assess mindfulness is to measure the degree to which individuals engage in formal mindfulness practices

conventional forms of measurement. Researchers have approached this several ways, and it is an aspect of the field that continues to develop. Some have attempted to measure mindfulness through objective or self-report monitoring of time spent in formal mindfulness practice, while others have attempted to assess resultant changes following a period of practice, or more enduring trait-like characteristics of a practitioner.

3.2.2   Mindfulness as a State

State mindfulness is the degree to which an individual is mindful in any given moment

Mindfulness is characterized in several ways, reflected in the many measures used in recent research to assess its changes or levels. It is sometimes characterized as a state of being during a particular moment in time, such that an individual, at a given moment, may be more or less mindful. According to this use of the term, and this approach to assessment, *being mindful* in a given moment does not necessarily require formal mindfulness practice; the extent of formal mindfulness practice may or may not predict mindful awareness in any given moment.

3.2.3   Mindfulness as a Trait

Trait mindfulness can be described as a person's overall tendency to be mindful across situations

The majority of mindfulness measures developed in contemporary psychology reflect a trait, or dispositional, conceptualization of mindfulness (these measures are reviewed later in this section). A trait can be defined as a quality or characteristic of an individual, with each person having a lesser or greater predisposition toward that trait in any given moment. In other words, similar to understanding of personality, some individuals have a greater tendency to have more instances of a certain characteristic, such as mindfulness (i.e., state mindfulness) and are thus often characterized as being a "mindful person" (i.e., trait mindfulness). Mindfulness, measured as a trait, has been shown to be highly correlated with other personality and psychological factors, such as neuroticism and conscientiousness (Siegling & Petrides, 2014), and facets associated with self-control and emotion regulation (Lyvers, Makin, Toms, Thorberg, & Samios, 2013). Measures of trait mindfulness tend to focus on an individual's typical way of responding or being. A paradoxical issue in the assessment of trait mindfulness is that as individuals become more mindful, or aware, of present experiences they also tend to become more aware that there are many periods in which they are not mindful. As such, individuals who begin practicing mindfulness and thus become aware of their own habitual lack of awareness, might report *lower* levels of trait mindfulness. This is likely to be most prevalent in early practitioners. Over time, however, there is some evidence suggesting that mindfulness practice may indeed lead to increases in measures of state mindfulness, which ultimately leads to increases in trait mindfulness, at least as we currently understand and assess it (Kiken, Garland, Bluth, Palsson, & Gaylord, 2015).

Despite an exponentially increasing number of scientific studies on mindfulness, there are several questions that remain unanswered. A recent area of inquiry is whether MBIs reliably increase trait mindfulness. Some studies have found evidence of increases in trait mindfulness (Bowen et al., 2009; Garland et al., 2015; Kiken et al., 2015) and other studies have found no changes in trait mindfulness (Bowen et al., 2014; Goldberg et al., 2015; Witkiewitz, Warner, et al., 2014). While this may reflect failure or lack of reliability of such programs and practices to affect an individual's tendencies or capacities to be mindful, difficulties in assessing mindfulness, as described in more detail below, may well be responsible (Davidson & Kaszniak, 2015; Grossman, 2011; Witkiewitz & Black, 2014).

3.2.4 Measures of Constructs Related to Mindfulness

There are numerous measures that are associated with the practice of mindfulness and may be used to indirectly measure the acquisition of mindfulness skills or changes in trait mindfulness. In Section 3.2.2 we review several biomarkers that have been shown to be impacted by mindfulness practice or robustly correlated with state and trait measures of mindfulness. In Section 3.2.3 we review behavioral measures of awareness, attention, and mind wandering (which may be considered the opposite of mindfulness). Self-report measures that were designed to assess constructs that are related to mindfulness, such as acceptance (Bond et al., 2011), self-compassion (Neff, 2003), mind wandering (Mrazek, Smallwood, & Schooler, 2012) and coping (Kato, 2012), are also available and are often used in empirical research examining MBIs.

3.3 Objective Measures of Mindfulness

For the purposes of this section, we consider any measure that does not require a subjective judgment or subjective response from an individual to be an objective measure. We review three different types of objective measures: passive measures, biomarkers, and behavioral assessments. Passive measures are assessments that do not require an active response from the individual being assessed. Biomarkers might require an active response on behalf of the individual (e.g., allowing blood to be drawn), but the measure obtained from the individual is an objective measure of some biological indicator (e.g., inflammatory response, cortisol level). Behavioral measures involve a behavioral response and the outcome of interest is typically a quantifiable behavioral indicator based on the demands of the measure (e.g., performance on a sustained attention task).

> There is a need for objective measures of mindfulness that do not rely on subjective judgments

3.3.1 Passive Measures of Mindfulness

New developments in biosensing technology, including the invention of numerous wearable devices and small sensors that can wirelessly communicate and provide constant data transfer, have great potential to impact the assessment of mindfulness, including the passive monitoring of mindfulness practice. Wireless accelerometers can be used to assess posture during meditation practice (Chang, Chen, Lee, Ching, & Huang, 2012) and many devices assess heart rate, breathing, and sleep cycles. Empirical research has not caught up with most of the new technologies at this point, yet numerous devices are now available and marketed to assist with meditation and assessing states of mind. For example, the Muse headband (http://www.choosemuse.com/, last accessed 7/1/2016), uses seven sensors to measure electrical brain activity, similar to an electroencephalography, and purportedly provides real time feedback about an individual's level of brain activity. The feedback is broad (e.g., neutral, calm) and we could not locate any peer-reviewed research articles to support the claims of the manufacturer, so it is unclear how well the feedback from the device corresponds to actual neural activity.

A great deal of research on passive monitoring devices is certainly necessary to assess the degree to which they could yield valid assessments of mindfulness practice and mindfulness states. Nonetheless, passively measuring activity, posture, breathing, and heart rate throughout the day and during mindfulness practice could potentially provide a wealth of data about an individual's engagement with formal and informal mindfulness practices, and could also be used to help therapists monitor progress in MBIs.

3.3.2   Biomarkers of Mindfulness

A biomarker (i.e., biological marker) is an objectively measured indicator of a biological state or biological process. Given the long-standing history of mind–body dualism, states of mind are often not directly characterized as biological; however, the practice of mindfulness, the state of mindfulness, and even the trait of mindfulness are inherently driven by biological processes. Like many psychological constructs there is not a single biological indicator of mindfulness, but there are many biological states and processes that have been shown to be associated with mindfulness practice, mindfulness states, and trait mindfulness. As such, these biomarkers could be useful tools in the assessment of mindfulness and the evaluation of MBIs. Importantly, different types of mindfulness practice and different states of mindfulness are likely associated with different biological processes (Lutz et al., 2015).

Focused attention on the breath is one of the central mindfulness practices in numerous meditation traditions. In some traditions, there is a deliberate slowing of the breath, whereas in other traditions the focus is on the sensations of breathing, without any intentional or voluntary changes to the breath. Either intentional slow paced breathing or even the careful observation of the breath can produce subtle changes in the breath, and there is evidence that mindfulness practice is associated with changes in respiration (Ahani et al., 2014). Notably studies have found that mindfulness practice tends to be associated with a shift toward slower paced breathing, which may be associated with increases in heart rate variability (Nesvold et al., 2012). Based on the available empirical evidence, we propose that measurement of changes in heart rate variability could be a biomarker with great potential in the assessment of mindfulness practice.

Mindfulness practice is ultimately a tool for training the mind (i.e., brain), and it is not surprising that there is a massive and rapidly expanding research literature examining the association between mindfulness and brain structure and function. Numerous theoretical models of neurobiological mechanisms of mindfulness have been proposed (Brewer, Elwafi, & Davis, 2013; Lutz et al., 2009; Slagter et al., 2011; Witkiewitz, Lustyk, & Bowen, 2013). Importantly, most of the research has focused on experienced long-term meditators, as compared to nonmeditators. Given potential differences in the neurobiology of individuals who initiate and maintain a long-term meditation practice, these studies must be interpreted with caution and provide very little information about the prospective neurobiological changes associated with training in mindfulness meditation. In general, nearly all of the research conducted to date has involved correlational studies and only a few experimental investigations with randomization to mindfulness meditation or no meditation control groups have been conducted.

At this point a single neurobiological marker of mindfulness practice, mindful states, and trait mindfulness has not been identified, but there are several neurobiological correlates of mindfulness among experienced and novice meditators that may be potential biomarkers. Changes in brain structure in the insula, orbitofrontal cortex, frontal cortex, hippocampus, and anterior cingulate cortices, have been identified across numerous studies (Fox et al., 2014; Hölzel, Carmody, et al., 2011; Lazar et al., 2005). Likewise, changes in brain activity and metabolism have been identified in the insula, anterior cingulate cortex, posterior cingulate cortex, right inferior frontal cortex, and bilateral cerebellum. Numerous other regions, spanning from the occipital lobe to the frontal lobe, have been found to be active during meditation states and have greater resting state functional connectivity with related regions among experienced meditators (Boccia, Piccardi, & Guariglia, 2015; Garrison et al., 2013; Pomykala et al., 2012; Sperduti, Martinelli, & Piolino, 2012; Tomasino, Chiesa, & Fabbro, 2014).

Research has found that mindfulness practice is linked to changes in both brain structure and function

Biological systems do not work independently, and there are strong, inherent, and necessary connections between the autonomic nervous system and central nervous system in regulating health and maintaining allostasis (Thayer & Sternberg, 2006). As such, it is not surprising that mindfulness is associated with respiration, cardiac functioning, neural functioning, and also immune function and other inflammatory processes. Early work by Davidson and colleagues found that eight weeks of MBSR was associated with improved immune function, as compared to a wait-list control group (Davidson et al., 2003). More recent work has documented multiple improvements in immune function, inflammatory processes, and even epigenetic changes associated with mindfulness meditation practice (Kaliman et al., 2014; Rosenkranz et al., 2012; Schutte & Malouff, 2014). We anticipate greater refinements of this work in the future and the excellent possibility for identifying genetic and/or inflammatory biomarkers that could be used to assess the effectiveness and efficacy of MBIs.

3.3.2   Behavioral Measures of Mindfulness

The development of new behavioral measures of mindfulness is a growing area of research and there are high expectations that well-validated and reliable behavioral measures will alleviate numerous problems in the measurement of mindfulness across studies (Davidson & Kaszniak, 2015; Goldberg et al., 2015; Grossman, 2011; Witkiewitz & Black, 2014)

In this section we review: (a) two new promising behavioral measures of mindfulness, breath counting, and tactile sensitivity, (b) a wealth of established behavioral measures of attentional processing and control, and (c) a group of behavioral mind wandering measures that are hypothesized to be the opposite of mindfulness.

The newest behavioral measure that was designed to explicitly assess the degree of present moment awareness during mindfulness is a novel breath counting tool (Levinson, Stoll, Kindy, Merry, & Davidson, 2014) that requires individuals to directly perceive the experience of breathing and be aware of breathing when it occurs. Using the tool, participants are instructed to count breaths from 1 to 9, pressing one button on a computer keyboard, mouse, or joystick for breaths 1–8 and then pressing another button on the 9th breath. The breath counting is then interrupted at random by three question probes assessing awareness and current breath count. Results from a validation study found the breath counting tool had excellent construct validity, as indicated by accuracy scores on the breath counting measure being highly correlated with self-reported trait mindfulness scores, and by the accuracy of breath counting both distinguishing experienced meditators from nonmeditators and showing increases in accuracy following mindfulness training. Importantly, the breath counting tool is really capturing only one aspect of mindfulness, present moment awareness, and might not be a good tool for assessing other aspects of mindfulness, including nonjudgment, compassion, and attentional control. In addition, future research using the measure will need to be conducted to further validate its use as a behavioral measure of mindfulness because only the developers of the measure have validated its use (Levinson et al., 2014).

The breath counting tool requires participants to press a button when they are aware of breathing a certain number of breaths

Tactile sensitivity is a behavioral measure that could be used to study the interoceptive awareness and attention aspects of mindfulness. One example of a measure of tactile sensitivity, the Somatic Signal Detection Task (Lloyd, Mason, Brown, & Poliakoff, 2008), involves a tactile pulse vibration sensation presented to the fingertip. Signal detection theory is used to determine the threshold of stimulus intensity at which participants report perceiving the vibration. Then repeated trials with and without the stimulus presented are conducted to determine the degree of misperception of the stimulus being presented and degree of tactile sensitivity. A recent study found that engaging in a brief body scan meditation, which involved listening to a 15 minute audio recording of body scan meditation per day for eight days, as compared to an audiobook control group, resulted in increased tactile sensitivity during the somatic signal detection task and reduced misperception of tactile sensations (Mirams, Poliakoff, Brown, & Lloyd, 2013). Interestingly the meditation and control groups did not differ on any of the self-report measures of attentional control or mindfulness that were hypothesized to show greater improvements in the meditation group.

The Somatic Signal Detection Task uses a subtle vibration sensation on the fingertip to measure awareness and attention

The practice of mindfulness meditation is often described as concentrative practice that requires great attentional control. As such, it is quite appropriate for behavioral measures of mindfulness to examine the attentional processing and control associated with mindfulness. Numerous behavioral measures of cognition and executive function have been used to assess aspects of attention, including the Sustained Attention to Response Task (Robertson, Manly, Andrade, Baddeley, & Yiend, 1997), a variety of continuous performance tests (Conners, 1985; Shalev, Ben-Simon, Mevorach, Cohen, & Tsal, 2011), and various signal detection and vigilance tasks (Epling, Russell, & Helton, 2015; Fleming & Lau, 2014; Smith & Ratcliff, 2009). A growing body of research has found mindfulness practice, even brief mindfulness training, is associated with improvements on behavioral measures of attention and executive functioning (Chiesa, Calati, & Serretti, 2011; Jha et al., 2007).

The breath counting tool, measures of tactile sensitivity, and attentional measures are direct behavioral measures of aspects of mindfulness, including present moment awareness, interoceptive awareness, and sustained attention, respectively. Another set of tools, behavioral measures of mind wandering (i.e., spontaneous cognition), are thought to measure the opposite of mindful attention (i.e., lack of mindfulness). Mind wandering has been a focus among cognitive psychologists and cognitive neuroscientists for several decades (Cohen, Hansel, & Sylvester, 1956), yet only recently have researchers begun to consider mind wandering as a construct that is likely to be strongly but inversely related to mindfulness (Mrazek et al., 2012; Smallwood, Mrazek, & Schooler, 2011). Numerous behavioral measures of mind wandering have been developed that typically involve engagement in one cognitively demanding task and then assessing the degree to which individuals remain on task or off task, often assessed via self-reported mind wandering (acknowledging when the mind has wandered), reaction time to words, or pupillometry during reading tasks (Franklin, Broadway, Mrazek, Smallwood, & Schooler, 2013; Franklin, Smallwood, & Schooler, 2011; Sayette, Schooler, & Reichle, 2010). There is a growing body of literature supporting the positive effects of brief mindfulness training on reductions in mind wandering via behavioral assessments (Banks, Welhaf, & Srour, 2015; Mrazek et al., 2012). Future research on MBIs for clinical populations should include behavioral assessments of mind wandering using pre- and posttreatment assessment batteries.

3.4   Self-Report Measures of Mindfulness

In this section we review several of the self-report measures that have been developed to assess different aspects of mindfulness. Numerous self-report measures have been developed and it is impossible to review all developed measures. Instead, we focus on some of the most widely used and widely studied measures and refer readers to comprehensive reviews and books that have evaluated and described numerous self-report measures of mindfulness (Baer et al., 2006; Baer, 2010, Park, Reilly-Spong, & Gross, 2013).

3.4.1   Self-Monitoring of Mindfulness Practice

In our clinical work and research we have used a simple paper-based form (Appendix 1: Mindfulness Practice Record), for encouraging participants to keep track of daily formal mindfulness practice and mindfulness of daily activ-

Smartphones can be used to track the frequency and length of mindfulness practices ities, including total minutes of formal practice and comments about practice. Other options for tracking practice include electronic diaries, spreadsheets, or a variety of mindfulness mobile applications (i.e., apps) keep track of practice sessions.

There are often two goals for encouraging self-monitoring of mindfulness practice. First, self-monitoring is a low threshold intervention for behavior change, and monitoring of behavior can increase behavior (in the case of monitoring healthy behaviors) or decrease behavior (in the case of monitoring unhealthy behaviors). In other words, the commitment to self-monitoring of mindfulness practice can help encourage practice. Second, self-monitoring can be used clinically and in research to assess level of engagement with the mindfulness practices. Clinically, we have observed occasions of self-monitored mindfulness practice often coincide with improvement in mood, decreases in unhealthy behaviors (e.g., drinking, smoking), and decreases in anger. It can be tremendously helpful for participants to see how mindfulness practices are associated with overall improvements in well-being.

3.4.2   State Measures of Mindfulness

State or direct measures of mindfulness assess self-reported states of mindfulness in the moment. The two most commonly used state measures of mindfulness are the Toronto Mindfulness Scale (Lau et al., 2006) and the state version of the Mindful Attention and Awareness Scale (Brown & Ryan, 2003). More recently, Tanay and Bernstein (2013) developed the State Mindfulness Scale, which was developed to test a broader conceptual model of mindfulness that was informed by traditional Buddhist scholarship.

Two popular measures of state mindfulness are the Toronto Mindfulness Scale and the state version of the Mindful Attention and Awareness Scale

The Toronto Mindfulness Scale (Lau et al., 2006) assesses "what you just experienced" across 13 items on a Likert-type scale from 0 = "not at all" to 4 = "very much," with items that are purported to assess two dimensions: decentering and curiosity. Example items that are purported to assess decentering include "I experienced myself as separate from my changing thoughts and feelings," and "I was aware of my thoughts and feelings without over-identifying with them." Example items that loaded on the curiosity dimension include "I was curious to see what my mind was up to from moment to moment," and "I was curious about my reactions to things." Psychometric testing of the Toronto Mindfulness Scale indicated excellent reliability and convergent validity (Lau et al., 2006). In addition, the Toronto Mindfulness Scale does appear to be sensitive to intervention effects with numerous studies finding increases in state mindfulness, as measured by the Toronto Mindfulness Scale, during and following MBIs (Bieling et al., 2012; Kiken et al., 2015; Lau et al., 2006).

The State version of the Mindful Attention and Awareness Scale (Brown & Ryan, 2003) assesses "to what degree were you having these experiences" across 5 items on a 7-point scale ranging from 0 = "not at all" to 6 = "very much." Example items include "I was doing things without paying attention," and "I was preoccupied with the future or the past." Initial psychometric testing of the state items from the Mindful Attention and Awareness Scale indicated excellent reliability and convergent validity (Brown & Ryan, 2003).

Brief mindfulness inductions have been shown to increase scores on items of state mindfulness from the Mindful Attention and Awareness Scale (Kiken & Shook, 2014; Ostafin & Kassman, 2012); however, it has not been evaluated as a measure of state mindfulness following longer duration MBIs.

The State Mindfulness Scale (Tanay & Bernstein, 2013) assesses perceived level of awareness and attention to the present experience during a pre-specified time period and context across 21 items on a 5-point Likert type scale from 0 = "not at all" to 5 = "very well." Example items include "I was aware of different emotions that arose in me," and "I noticed physical sensations come and go." The 21 items load on two related subscales: mindfulness of the body and mindfulness of the mind. Initial testing of the State Mindfulness Scale indicated acceptable reliability and convergent validity, and scores on the State Mindfulness Scale were shown to increase during a mindfulness-based intervention (Tanay & Bernstein, 2013). The scores on the State Mindfulness Scale were moderately correlated with scores on the Toronto Mindfulness Scale, but were not related to scores on the Mindful Attention and Awareness Scale.

Future research should examine incremental and predictive validity among these three state measures of mindfulness, as well as sensitivity to change during mindfulness-based interventions. Studies have generally found scores on the Toronto Mindfulness Scale and State Mindfulness Scale to reliably increase following MBIs (Bieling et al., 2012; Kiken et al., 2015; Lau et al., 2006; Tanay & Bernstein, 2013); however, there is less evidence in support of the State version of the Mindful Attention and Awareness Scale as a measure of self-reported state mindfulness that could be used to measure increases in state mindfulness following MBIs.

3.4.3   Trait Measures of Mindfulness

There are currently at least ten widely used measures of dispositional or trait mindfulness that each assess multiple constructs related to mindfulness (Park et al., 2013; Rau & Williams, 2016). Many of the available instruments have been translated into a variety of languages and have been adapted for a variety of populations. We review each of these measures briefly and provide original citations for each measure for interested readers.

The Mindful Attention and Awareness Scale (Brown & Ryan, 2003) was the first widely used measure of trait mindfulness. The scale includes 15 items representing a unidimensional mindfulness construct. The reliability and validity of the Mindful Attention and Awareness Scale has been supported in a number of studies (Park et al., 2013; Rau & Williams, 2016).

The Five Facet Mindfulness Questionnaire (Baer et al., 2006) is the most widely used measure of trait mindfulness. It was developed by factor analyzing the combined item pool from five different mindfulness instruments, the Mindful Attention and Awareness Scale, the Kentucky Inventory of Mindfulness Skills, the Freiburg Mindfulness Inventory, the Southampton Mindfulness Questionnaire, and the Cognitive and Affective Mindfulness Scale. The Five Facet Mindfulness Questionnaire includes 39 items that assess five facets of mindfulness: acting with awareness, observing, describing, nonreactivity, and nonjudging of inner experience. Internal consistency reliability and construct

The Five Facet Mindfulness Questionnaire integrates items from several existing measures

validity of the Five Facet Mindfulness Questionnaire has been supported across numerous studies (Park et al., 2013); however, there is mixed evidence regarding whether the Five Facet Mindfulness Questionnaire is sensitive to changes following MBIs (Bowen et al., 2009; Goldberg et al., 2015). Shortened versions of the scale, including a 20 item version (Tran, Glück, & Nader, 2013 a 24 item version (Bohlmeijer, ten Klooster, Fledderus, Veehof, & Baer, 2011), have demonstrated good reliability and validity (Bohlmeijer et al., 2011; Tran et al., 2013).

The Kentucky Inventory of Mindfulness Skills (Baer, Smith, & Allen, 2004) contains 39 items measuring four distinct mindfulness skills: observing, describing, acting with awareness, and accepting without judgment. It has shown mixed reliability and validity (Park et al., 2013), and it has generally been replaced in many studies by the newer and more psychometrically sound Five Facet Mindfulness Questionnaire.

The Freiburg Mindfulness Inventory (Walach, Buchheld, Buttenmuller, Kleinknecht, & Schmidt, 2006) contains 14 items that appear to assess trait mindfulness on two dimensions: acceptance and presence (Kohls, Sauer, & Walach, 2009). Numerous studies have found support for the reliability and validity of the Freiburg Mindfulness Inventory (Park et al., 2013); however, in our own research, scores on the Freiburg Mindfulness Inventory did not increase following MBRP (Witkiewitz, Warner et al., 2014).

The Cognitive and Affective Mindfulness Scale – Revised (Feldman, Hayes, Kumar, Greeson, & Laurenceau, 2007) is a 12-item measure that assesses four dimensions of mindfulness: acceptance, attention, awareness, and present focus. The revision is recommended by the developers in lieu of the original scale. The revised scale has shown good reliability and validity across studies (Park et al., 2013; Rau & Williams, 2016).

The Philadelphia Mindfulness Scale (Cardaciotto, Herbert, Forman, Moitra, & Farrow, 2008) is a 20-item measure that assesses mindfulness on two dimensions: awareness and acceptance. The two subscales are recommended over the use of a total score, and the reliability and validity of the two subscale measure has been supported (Park et al., 2013). A short form version with only 10 items has been developed and showed excellent psychometric properties in two samples (Zeng, Li, Zhang, & Liu, 2015).

The Southampton Mindfulness Questionnaire (Chadwick et al., 2008) is a 16-item measure that was designed to assess awareness of distressing thoughts and images along four dimensions: letting go, nonaversion, nonjudgment, and observation. There is evidence of reliability and validity of the Southampton Mindfulness Questionnaire and scores on the measure are higher in meditators as compared to nonmeditators (Park et al., 2013). However, the scale was not sensitive to changes following a mindfulness-based intervention for psychosis (van der Valk, van de Waerdt, Meijer, van den Hout, & de Haan, 2013).

The Experiences Questionnaire (Fresco et al., 2007) was designed to measure *decentering*, defined as "the ability to observe ones thoughts and feelings as temporary, objective events in the mind, as opposed to reflections of the self that are necessarily true" (p. 234; Fresco et al., 2007). Fresco and colleagues (2007) characterize decentering as a related construct to mindfulness, but not synonymous with mindfulness. The Experiences Questionnaire contains 20 items and has been shown to have adequate reliability and validity (Park et al., 2013). In addition, there is evidence that the Experiences Questionnaire may be sensitive to intervention effects with increases in decentering observed following MBCT (Bieling et al., 2012).

The Toronto Mindfulness Scale – Trait Version (Davis, Lau, & Cairns, 2009) is a modified version of the Toronto Mindfulness Scale that was designed to assess dispositional mindfulness, rather than moment-to-moment states of experience. The same 13 items from the original version of the Toronto Mindfulness Scale are included and they are still purported to assess two dimensions: decentering and curiosity. The instructions were modified from "We are interested in what you just experienced" to "We are interested in your day to day experience" and some items were modified slightly to represent more trait-like experiences of mindfulness. The Trait Version of the scale has shown good reliability and validity, as well as modest to strong correlations with existing measures of trait mindfulness (Davis et al., 2009).

The Mindfulness/Mindlessness Scale (Haigh, Moore, Kashdan, & Fresco, 2011) is a 21-item measure based on a cognitive-information processing framework, proposed by Langer (Langer, 1989), that examines four interrelated dimensions: novelty seeking, engagement, novelty producing, and flexibility. The measure has been shown to have good construct validity and reliability of the total score; however, the reliability of the four subscales are poor (below 0.70). A nine-item shortened version has also been developed (Haigh et al., 2011), but it has not yet been tested by other applied researchers.

3.4.4   Related Measures to Assess Processes in Mindfulness-Based Interventions

There are numerous additional self-report measures that were designed to assess constructs related to mindfulness such as acceptance (Bond et al., 2011), self-compassion (Neff, 2003), mind wandering (Mrazek et al., 2012), and coping flexibility (Kato, 2012). These measures may also be incorporated into clinical research and practice to assess the efficacy of MBIs.

More recently, the Applied Mindfulness Process Scale (Li, Black, & Garland, 2016) was developed to directly measure the targeted processes of change in MBIs. The Applied Mindfulness Process Scale is a 15-item measure that includes items assessing the degree to which mindfulness practices can be used in daily lives (e.g., "I used mindfulness practice to be aware of and appreciate pleasant events"). Construct validation of the measure (Li et al., 2016) has identified three subscales, labeled as decentering, positive emotion regulation, and negative emotion regulation. The three subscales and total score have been shown to be associated with other measures of mindfulness as well as moderately correlated with amount of time spent in meditation. The Applied Mindfulness Process Scale has been validated across three studies, but has not yet been examined as a process measure during a mindfulness-based intervention.

The Applied Mindfulness Process Scale detects mindfulness-related processes of change post intervention

4

Treatment

4.1   Overview and Treatment Rationale

Mindfulness-based interventions (MBIs) target a range of clinical mechanisms and outcomes, and thus teach skills that may vary across interventions. Despite variations in protocols, evidence-based mindfulness interventions were all similarly designed with a common goal: They aim to introduce mindfulness practice as a way to increase awareness and skillful means to reduce suffering. Training in mindfulness practice is the central component, instructing participants to continually return their focus to the direct experience of the present moment.

A central training in MBIs, drawn from Buddhist teachings, is discernment between the direct experiences of *pain*, which is unavoidable in all sentient beings, from what is added to those experiences that can result in *suffering*. Pain results from the direct experience of thoughts, emotions, and sensations that arise from moment-to-moment. Suffering comes from automatic and habitual reactions to aversive experience. Such reactions may come in the form of stories about what is occurring, rumination, attempts to avoid the experience, and/or desire to hold onto or seek out pleasant experiences. The training included in MBIs is intended to increase mindful awareness and nonjudgmental acceptance of all experience, while also reducing suffering that comes from attempts to avoid or attach to these experiences. Inquiry, or the verbal exploration between the facilitator and participants following the practices, is used to highlight and reinforce this learning.

> Distinguishing between the direct experience of *pain* and the resulting *suffering* is a core feature of many MBIs

4.2   Therapeutic Approach

The learning that occurs in MBIs is of course largely a function of the mindfulness practices on which they are based. However, the curious and nonjudgmental approach participants are learning in relation to their own experiences is also reinforced by the facilitator's stance. Skillful delivery includes embodiment of these characteristics. In this section, we review what are widely considered essential elements of a facilitator's therapeutic style, as well as provide recommendations for introducing mindfulness practices and facilitating mindful inquiry (Shonin et al., 2013).

4.2.1   Importance of Personal Practice

The practice of mindfulness is a continual, personal investigation of present moment experiences that can destabilize habitual response patterns that lead to inflexible and narrow behavioral repertoires, and ultimately increase suffering. Mindfulness practice allows one to stay in contact with the present moment, with a sustained, nondefensive, and nonreactive awareness that supports the development of alternative, more adaptive and skillful behaviors (Hayes et al., 2012). This dynamic process of mindfulness cannot be taught to others in an authentic, effective way without the facilitator being firmly established in his or her own personal mindfulness practice. Embodied mindfulness is the primary vehicle for teaching (Kabat-Zinn, 2003).

Developing a personal mindfulness practice is an essential step in becoming a mindfulness facilitator

The facilitators' personal experience with mindfulness assists others' cultivation of mindfulness in several ways. While teaching, the facilitator must remain open to the present moment and mindfully respond to what is happening in the room – welcoming all pleasant, unpleasant, and neutral experiences with equanimity. The facilitator must be intimately familiar with his or her own habits of mind, especially the impulse to fill an empty space, challenge the skeptic, or avoid, diminish, or fix painful or difficult experiences – all responses that are likely to be attached to preconceived outcomes. The facilitator must also embrace the quintessence of *beginner's mind* and relinquish the need to be known as an authority or expert. This attitude will guide the facilitator to be curious, compassionate, and flexible in responding mindfully to whatever happens in the room. This mindful approach to teaching invites the facilitator to incorporate a delicate balance of *knowing and not knowing*. Finally, an honest, open, and full awareness of the present moment requires trust in the practice, in the silent moments, in the shared experience of human suffering, and in all individuals' potential for growth. These skills and an embodied, trusting understanding are developed through a dedicated and sustained personal mindfulness practice (McCown, Reibel, & Micozzi, 2011).

A comprehensive meta-analysis demonstrated that therapists' personal experience with mindfulness practice, and not their general clinical training, moderated clinical outcomes at the end of treatment (Khoury, Lecomte, Fortin, et al., 2013). Results suggest that a facilitator's own mindfulness practice may influence clinical outcomes. Unfortunately, at least one study indicated divergence in practice from these standard recommendations. In a small sample ($n = 116$) of mental health therapists who provided MBIs to trauma-exposed clinical populations, less than half of the MBI therapists reported maintaining a personal practice, and only 9% reported a daily practice (Waelde, Thompson, Robinson, & Iwanicki, 2016).

Competency in teaching mindfulness is a combination of intellectual understanding and an embodied personal knowing. It is only with an intimate, personal mindfulness practice that a facilitator can truly assist others in their understanding and cultivation of mindfulness. Therefore, it is imperative that those who teach mindfulness remain committed to their own personal mindfulness practice and continually participate in classes and periodic retreats to develop and deepen their practice (Kabat-Zinn, 2003).

4.2.2 Motivational Interviewing Style

Motivational interviewing (MI; Miller & Rollnick, 2013) is a client-centered conversation style for eliciting and strengthening behavior change. Adopting a motivational interviewing therapeutic style can be effective and congruous with the intentions of a mindfulness-based approach. Accordingly, we review key concepts in MI and explore how they relate to facilitating MBIs.

Several concepts and practices from motivational interviewing are useful when facilitating mindfulness

Collaboration
Collaboration with the participant is essential to facilitating MBIs. In a MBI, the person leading the group is often referred to as the *facilitator* rather than the teacher or therapist, and the individual seeking services is a *participant* in the process, versus a client or patient. The facilitator is one who guides participants through various mindfulness practices and facilitates participants' learning from their own experiences. Instruction in particular mindfulness skills is balanced with an overall collaborative spirit and exploration of experiences.

The readiness for, and learning and practicing of, mindfulness may be very different across individuals. For example, for some, a focus on intensive formal mindfulness meditation is most appropriate, while for others, metaphors and structured exercises that focus on specific mindfulness skills may be best.

Rolling With Resistance
Rolling with resistance is an approach for responding to participant resistance, including resistance to changing a given behavior, attending therapy, or engaging in homework exercises or skills reviewed in therapy. Rolling with resistance encourages the facilitator to seek to understand a participant and collaboratively develop solutions versus attacking, confronting, or arguing with a participant, which often lead to *push back* and can increase defensiveness. As an MBI facilitator, it can be effective to *roll with* participant resistance rather than trying to convince or *sell* these approaches and practices to a participant, or convince them of a particular point of view.

It can be counterproductive to forcefully persuade a participant to practice mindfulness

Acceptance
According to the developers of MI (Miller & Rollnick, 2013), an attitude of acceptance involves respecting participants, honoring their uniqueness and potential, seeking to understand their internal perspective and experiences through accurate empathy, respecting their autonomy, and acknowledging their strengths. The attitude of acceptance conveyed by the developers of MI is aligned with the qualities of openness and nonjudgment that are cultivated through mindfulness practice. Practicing and embodying these qualities is crucial to fostering and communicating this spirit of acceptance.

Mindfulness practice often involves *turning towards* and *staying with* discomfort and may require guiding participants through practices that heighten their awareness of difficult or distressing thoughts, emotions, and sensations. The ability to accurately empathize is an important element in facilitating an MBI. One participant's experience during a mindfulness practice may differ greatly from another's, depending on factors such as culture, life experiences, personality traits, and personal preferences. It is important to be aware of and explore this with participants, rather than assuming participants experienced typical or similar internal phenomena.

Reflective Listening

Reflective listening skills, fundamental to MI, are also useful when facilitating MBIs. Either simple or complex reflections can be used to convey accurate empathy toward a participant. A *simple reflection* may be used to restate or paraphrase the basic message shared by a speaker, whereas *complex reflections* are used to include additional content in reflective statements intended to capture the deeper meaning and/or emotional experience that the participant may be experiencing. For example, a participant may share the following in reference to practicing mindfulness at home:

- *Participant:* I have been so busy lately and it has been hard to practice mindfulness. I know it has been helpful for me before, and I know practicing it is important but I just can't seem to find the time to do it. I don't know what's wrong with me. I want to try to find a way to make this group work for me.

Immediately lecturing the participant about the importance of home practice or quickly starting to problem solve with the participant is often ineffective and can reduce trust and alliance. Reflective listening may be a more effective initial approach, and can convey acceptance and understanding of the participant's experience. Here are a few examples:

- *Facilitator (simple reflection):* You're having trouble fitting finding time to fit mindfulness practice into your busy life. You want to make it work and you're not quite sure where to go from here.
- *Facilitator (complex reflection):* It seems you're having difficulty finding the time for mindfulness practice. At the same time you really want to find a way to practice. I'm also wondering whether you have been noticing judgmental or self-critical thoughts towards yourself about not practicing.

Here one might be tuning into the participants statement of, "I don't know what's wrong with me" (and perhaps the participant's tone and body language) to reflect additional thoughts and feelings that may underlie the participant's statements. Complex reflections involve making educated guesses or hypotheses about the participant's experience, informed by the participant's words, tone, and body language and the listener's genuine sense of what the participant is trying to communicate or what she or he may be experiencing. It is important to note, however, that it is acceptable for a hypothesis to be wrong. Regardless of whether a complex reflection is on target, complex reflections convey that the listener is genuinely trying to understand what the participant is communicating and experiencing. Additionally, when a complex reflection is somewhat off target, participants have an opportunity to clarify what they are feeling, which can ultimately result in them feeling better understood.

Another aspect of bringing acceptance to participants is to notice and acknowledge their willingness and awareness in a genuine and heartfelt manner (e.g., "I appreciate your willingness to experiment with these mindfulness practices we have been learning" or "You have been working hard at incorporating these practices into your everyday life"). During the inquiry process, described in more detail in Section 4.2.5, comments that affirm the willingness of a participant to share his or her experience and that convey acceptance and nonjudgment reinforce the approach that MBIs encourage participants to take towards themselves. This could involve a simple statement such as, "I appreciate your willingness to share your experiences of that practice."

Evocation

Another core element of MI is evocation (Miller & Rollnick, 2013), or *bringing forth* strengths, abilities, thoughts, and insights already present in the individual in some form. MI encourages the use of open-ended questions and statements that invite and encourage a participant to share thoughts and perspectives on important and relevant issues.

Embracing this spirit can likewise be helpful in MBI facilitation. Participants inherently have the capacity for mindful awareness, and mindfulness practice brings this to light and strengthens these abilities and skills. Participants may recognize experiences in which they have had present-centered awareness, such as savoring a delicious meal or watching a sunset. They may share comments such as, "Before this, I didn't realize that I was at times actually practicing mindfulness, and now I know that is exactly what I was doing!"

Evocation can be helpful when introducing mindfulness practice and exploring its application to specific challenges with participants. For example, rather than trying to persuade a participant that mindfulness can be helpful, the mindfulness facilitator might ask an open-ended question such as, "How do you see mindfulness fitting in with your life?" or "What are your ideas about how mindfulness is related to substance abuse?"

> Asking open-ended questions is an effective method for engaging participants and sparking interactive discussions

The specific MI technique called *Elicit-Provide-Elicit* may be particularly useful when introducing mindfulness practice to participants (Miller & Rollnick, 2013). The technique involves 3 basic steps: (1) elicit what the participant already knows and wants to know, (2) provide information in a relatively neutral manner, and (3) elicit the participant's thoughts and interpretations about the information provided. Before introducing any ideas or theories about mindfulness, it can be helpful to ask participants what they experience in an initial introductory practice, to call upon their experience and knowledge. For example, following a basic experiential introduction to mindfulness, the facilitator can elicit the participant's reflection on her or his experience. For example, "Given what you just experienced in that practice, how would you describe mindfulness?" Asking open-ended questions and eliciting experiences and comments from group members can foster a more active interest and engagement in the group, and can highlight the participants' inherent ability and knowledge, versus implying that there is a deficit to be remedied by the facilitator.

4.2.3   Modeling Qualities of Mindfulness

There are many approaches to learning about mindfulness. Some individuals learn by listening to didactic instruction from a teacher or reading about mindfulness, by engaging in mindfulness practices, or by learning experientially by receiving feedback and coaching from a teacher. Participants can also learn about the qualities and essence of mindfulness by observing behaviors mod-

Modeling qualities
of mindfulness
helps participants
understand what
mindfulness means
and how it is
practiced

eled by an MBI facilitator. It is essential for a facilitator to actively model the qualities that are being fostered and supported in participants. The following are specific attitudes and behaviors that MBI facilitators can use when teaching mindfulness.

Curiosity

Curiosity in the context of an MBI involves bringing a *beginner's mind* to one's experience; that is, *noticing what is present as if seeing it for the first time*. Curiosity involves an interest and willingness to actively explore and understand what an experience means, whether internal, such as thoughts, sensations, and emotions, or external, such as objects or events in the environment. Curiosity can facilitate a focus on present-moment experience, and it fosters a willingness to approach and explore a range of experiences, even those that are perceived as difficult or unwanted. Rather than attempting to force attention, curiosity can facilitate a more natural and less effortful way of staying present and relating to an experience. The MBI facilitator can model this curiosity in a number of ways. During inquiry and group discussion, the facilitator may actively demonstrate curiosity with statements such as, "That's really interesting – may I ask you a little more about that?" or "I'm curious about whether you noticed any body sensations related to that feeling of frustration," or "I'm wondering, have you noticed this about your mind before?" After a mindfulness practice, the facilitator can initiate discussion with a spirit of curiosity, such as "I am really curious what you all noticed during that practice." Modeling this curiosity may be most important when participants share distressing or difficult experiences. This can encourage participants to actively explore their direct experience rather than getting caught up in *stories* or judgments about their experience. By observing curiosity in the facilitator, participants learn to bring curiosity to their own experiences, including experiences that may have typically been avoided. It is critical, however, to bring genuine curiosity rather than a forced or *demonstrated* curiosity, which is likely to be perceived as insincere. A facilitator's personal mindfulness practice naturally fosters curiosity, and the facilitator may draw upon his or her own inner capacity to bring a curious and present moment focus to all experiences of the participants.

Appropriate and
genuine self-
disclosure can be
effective in modeling
an attitude of
curiosity

Appropriate self-disclosure can also be used, skillfully and moderately, to model curiosity. For example, during a mindful eating practice the facilitator might say, "I always notice something different about the raisin even though I've done this practice many times. Today I was really aware of the texture of this particular raisin." It is vital to share genuine and heartfelt comments about actual direct experience, and not simply say something inauthentic for the sake of attempting to model a given attitude or behavior.

Nonjudgment

Bringing a curious, open, and nonjudgmental attitude towards one's experience is at the heart of mindfulness practice. When we practice mindful awareness of whatever is arising in the present moment, we are strengthening the intention and ability to bring this nonjudgmental and nonevaluative stance towards our experience in order to see things as they really are, rather than seeing things through the lens of our judgments and past experience. Cultivating nonjudgment towards our experiences and ourselves can be a powerful antidote to the potentially destructive human tendency to be critical towards ourselves and immediately judge ourselves or our experience as good or bad. Mindfulness practice often involves noticing judgmental thoughts as they arise, and doing our best not to judge our own tendency to judge, which often only serves to perpetuate further suffering.

Modeling an attitude of openness and nonjudgment is an effective way to facilitate the cultivation of these mindfulness qualities in participants. A facilitator can model openness and nonjudgment through his or her overall demeanor and style of interacting with participants (e.g., adopting the MI style described in the prior section). These qualities can also be modeled through specific responses and interactions with participants during the inquiry process. Facilitator responses can convey that all participant experiences will be honored and respected equally, and that there is no *right* way to feel when engaging in mindfulness practice. Individual participants may share a range of different experiences, both within and across various mindfulness practices. For example, following the body scan practice, a participant might share, "I felt relaxed and focused," whereas another participant might say, "I was bored most of the time, and I kept getting distracted." Yet another participant might comment, "I felt anxious and I couldn't stop focusing on the pain in my back." In response to these diverse direct experiences, the facilitator can bring an equal level of acceptance, interest, and curiosity to each of these unique experiences; this conveys the message that all experiences are acceptable, that it is okay to share these experiences, and that the facilitator is equally interested in and curious about each of them, including experiences that seem very different from the rest of the group or are perhaps distressing and unwanted by the participant. A simple and genuine "thank you" can convey acceptance, appreciation, and nonjudgment towards participants and their experiences.

In some cases, the facilitator may ask certain questions or provide statements that actively invite and encourage participants to share any and all experiences, and to reiterate that there is no right way to feel. For example, "I'm wondering if anyone had a different experience during the practice and perhaps noticed things such as frustration or boredom, or something else." In a group setting, sometimes several participants in a row will share similar experiences (e.g., feeling relaxed or liking the practice) and other participants may then feel hesitant or uncomfortable about sharing different experiences (e.g., mind wandering, restlessness) because the facilitator or other group members might judge them. In these cases, it can be particularly helpful to pose a question that communicates openness and curiosity toward all types of experiences, and not just *good* or *right* responses. Appropriate self-disclosure can also be effective in normalizing certain experiences. For example, during inquiry following an in-session practice, a facilitator might comment, "Mind wandering can be very common during these practices. During that last practice, I noticed my own mind wandering and thoughts popping up about various things. Did anyone notice their mind wandering during the practice?" Or, when discussing challenges related to implementing mindfulness in one's life, a facilitator might offer, "Sometimes when I first sit down to practice, my mind starts thinking about all the other things I could be doing. Have you noticed similar experiences, or any other challenges when practicing mindfulness?"

Modeling openness and nonjudgment is very important when participants share experiences arising from a mindfulness practice

Flexibility in Mindfulness Practice

The MBI facilitator endeavors to model flexibility and applicability of mindfulness practice. A key aspect of this is the ability to bring mindfulness to different types of daily situations, often *on the fly*. A skillful facilitator may use challenging situations that occur within sessions to demonstrate how mindful practice can be flexibly used to respond to various situations, such as loud and disruptive noises in the background, or participants arguing or becoming upset with each other. These can be opportune moments to encourage and guide practices to model how these skills can be used flexibly. For example, a facilitator might say:

> I am wondering if we might just take a moment right now to pause and notice what is happening. This is interesting. If you are willing, take a minute to close your eyes and observe what is happening right now… Noticing how your body feels, noticing thoughts and emotions that are present, maybe noticing how difficult it can be to just pause here and be with discomfort … And then maybe connecting with your breath for a few moments, noticing the sensations of your breath as it goes in and out. Then when you are ready, opening your eyes if they're closed and bringing your attention back to the group. I'm curious – what did you notice?

4.2.4   Guidelines for Leading Mindfulness Practices

MBI facilitators draw upon several skills, including embodiment of curiosity and flexibility. Facilitators also offer guidance of formal and informal mindfulness practices. The following are tips for leading the mindfulness practices included in MBIs.

Offer Choices

When leading mindfulness practices, it is helpful to clarify that participants are free to practice in a way that facilitates their own awareness and safety. Providing participants with a range of choices will support their autonomy and increase self-efficacy for practice. First, the facilitator can clarify that participants have a choice to practice with their eyes open, half open, or closed. This can be essential to participants' sense of safety. Second, the facilitator may note that participants can adjust their physical posture to whatever position works to best suit their own bodies and limitations. Postures include sitting cross-legged or kneeling on the floor with a cushion, sitting in a chair, standing, or lying down or walking when indicated. At the beginning of leading a mindfulness practice in a group setting the facilitator might offer, "When you are ready, come to a comfortable position – one that will support you as we engage in this practice. You can choose a position that works for you, such as sitting on the floor with a cushion, or using a chair, closing your eyes if that helps bring awareness to our experience, or keeping your eyes open if that is more comfortable."

Closing one's eyes during a mindfulness practice is optional; participants should feel free to keep their eyes open if they prefer

Practice While Guiding

When leading a mindfulness practice, the facilitator is also engaging in the practice. The experience of doing a practice oneself while guiding others is different than doing a practice alone. However, it becomes easier with practice. Practicing along with participants while guiding involves shifting between focusing on the facilitator's own experience, providing verbal instruction, and taking moments to monitor the room. For instance, there will be times in which the facilitator is primarily focused on providing verbal instruction, especially at the beginning of the practices. However, moments of silence during guidance can provide an opportunity to reconnect with the practice and one's own experience. This allows the facilitator to draw upon direct moment-to-moment experience to inform guidance, authentically modeling the process of practicing mindfulness while providing verbal instruction. Throughout the practice, the facilitator is also periodically monitoring participants to gauge how they are doing.

Engaging in the exercise while guiding, the facilitator can draw from direct experience and guide in an authentic manner

The facilitator draws from direct experience to offer *possibilities* describing what participants may notice, while also being careful to not impose that direct experience on others. For example, if the facilitator notices sensations of tingling and warmth in her hands during a body scan, she might suggest, "Notice any sensations in your hands, perhaps tingling, warmth, or coolness." If she notices her own mind is busy with thoughts in a given moment of a practice, she might offer, "You may notice your mind wandering at times and different thoughts popping up. See if you can observe that thoughts are arising, and then gently bring your attention back to the sensations of breathing."

Because drawing from direct experience is essential while guiding mindfulness practices, directly reading from a script is not recommended. Becoming competent and confident in guiding others takes practice. There is simply no substitute for one's own dedicated personal mindfulness practice, as facilitators without direct experience of practice are not properly informed nor equipped to guide others. Before leading practices for participants, a facilitator might practice guiding various meditations with friends, family, or colleagues. Exposure to guided instruction by other experienced mindfulness facilitators can be helpful as well. Facilitators may read examples of guidance from books, meditation audio recordings, or attend mindfulness classes. Exposure to various mindfulness facilitators can provide several models for leading practices, and offer different styles of leading. The facilitator is also encouraged to adopt a personal style of leading mindfulness-based on her or his own experience, however, rather than seeking to perfectly match the way others lead mindfulness.

A skilled facilitator connects with the spirit and intentions of mindfulness practice and develops her/his own style of leading

Language

The way in which language is used can convey fundamental, yet sometimes subtle or misunderstood, aspects of practices in MBIs. Below are some guidelines about specific language that can be useful when guiding the practices in the context of an MBI. While having a general understanding of what language can be effective is certainly important, remembering exact words or phrases is not. The facilitator will develop a general sense for useful words and phrases, and then gradually expand to a broader repertoire and flexibility of language over time. A skilled MBI facilitator:

- Uses language that supports autonomy and provides participants with choices, e.g., *when you are ready, if you like, if you choose.*
- Incorporates *present moment* language in your instruction, e.g., *right now, this moment, moment to moment, here and now.*

- Avoids language that makes assumptions about how participants should feel, or that tells them how to try to feel. For example, statements such as, "notice how relaxing it feels to take in a deep breath of air" tell a participant how they *should feel*, rather than giving them instructions on how to *notice whatever they might be feeling*. Language more useful to this process and training might be, "bringing awareness, as best you can, to whatever sensations you might notice in the body as you breathe."

- Uses language that reflects the wide range of what individuals may be experiencing, and reminds them that there is not one *right* or expected way to feel, e.g., "Perhaps you notice sensation here, or perhaps you really don't feel much at all …. you may be experiencing discomfort or restlessness, or maybe you are noticing something different."

- Uses language such as *notice, observe, bring curiosity to, direct your attention to, watch, explore, tune into, feel, recognize,* that represent the intention of MBI practices. Facilitators are helping participants learn how to bring awareness to what is actually happening, versus trying to change or suggest what should be happening.

- Asks questions that evoke curiosity, such as *Where is your attention right now? What is going on with your thoughts right now? Where do you feel your breathing most clearly in your body?*

- Incorporates language that invites participants to the *possibility* of bringing an open and nonjudgmental attitude to their experience rather than telling them to do so, or assuming that this is easy to do. It can be helpful to use *softeners* such as: *seeing if you can, allowing yourself, as best you can, exploring what is would be like to, see if it is possible to.*

- Uses words and phrases useful for facilitating openness and nonjudgment, such as *allowing, opening up to, making room for, gently acknowledging, sitting with, being with, bringing an openhearted attitude to.*

The following are examples of complete phrases that combine softeners and language to facilitate openness and nonjudgment: "as best as you can allowing yourself to feel whatever feelings are present for you right now" or "exploring what it is like to bring an openhearted attitude to each moment, opening up to your experience and acknowledging whatever may be arising."

4.2.5   Inquiry

Inquiry is a process in which a facilitator engages participants in a collaborative and interactive verbal exploration of their experiences and observations following each mindfulness practice. Contrary to behavioral change strategies or didactic lectures, the facilitator models a curious, interested, accepting stance toward the participants' experiences, regardless of the content (Segal, Williams, & Teasdale, 2002).

The process of inquiry serves several purposes. While it aims to cultivate a safe environment for participants to share observations, inquiry also assists participants in adopting their own curiosity and openness to their experiences. This modeling contributes to participants' cultivation of self-compassion and diminished reactivity, internal self-critical cognitions, and their attempts to avoid aversive experiences. Additionally, participants learn to anchor their learning in specific, personal experience rather than in generalized intellectual concepts and theories. From this vantage point, the facilitator has the opportunity to link participants' personal observations and discoveries to the learning themes of the program. Finally, discussions concerning perceived obstacles and barriers to practice are a critical element of the inquiry. Participants may state that they had trouble practicing because they were distracted by wandering minds, or bombarded by negative or self-critical thoughts. A facilitator might respond by simply encouraging participants to notice and take an interest in these experiences, while refraining from attempts to eliminate the obstacles, or provide suggestions for the participant to be more "successful" with the practices. This process normalizes common obstacles inherent to practicing mindfulness. When practicing in groups, the facilitator can use the group format to highlight automated and unrecognized habits of thought, as well as universal patterns of thinking (Crane et al., 2015; Felder, Dimidjian, & Segal, 2012).

Inquiry is often described as one of the most difficult and crucial aspects of MBIs (Crane et al., 2015). Primary guidance for leading mindful inquiry is often conveyed in the metaphor of three concentric circles. In the center circle, the facilitator inquires by asking a very open question, "What did you notice?" This personal circle highlights the importance of starting with each person's direct present-moment experience. In the second circle, the facilitator asks how the practice was different from typical, automatic ways of behaving. In the final circle, the facilitator inquires how the practice may be relevant to the larger aim of the group/treatment (e.g., reducing depression, stress, or anxiety), thereby relating each participant's experience to the session's key teaching points. The inquiry process is a mindfulness practice in and of itself. Relatedly, the facilitator's authentic, embodied understanding of mindfulness is imperative to skillfully engage in this process (Crane et al., 2015; Segal et al., 2002).

The inquiry process following guided mindfulness practices is a key component of MBIs

4.3   Incorporation of Poetry, Metaphors, Imagery, and Storytelling

In addition to personal practice and the ability to engage in mindful inquiry, an MBI facilitator must also have the capacity to think conceptually about the experience of mindfulness. The facilitator must be able to respond to a question or observation from a participant from a theoretical understanding of how individuals learn, grow, and develop their mindfulness practices. A key feature of mindfulness is the *de-literalization* of language and cognition; this is important because the nature of mindfulness can be difficult to convey in ordinary language. Therefore, poems, metaphors, storytelling, and imagery are often used to facilitate the understanding and cultivation of mindfulness. These tools can be an "alternative vehicle for communicating this different relationship to experience" that mindfulness requires (Segal et al., 2002, p. 221). These techniques are beneficial for reaching participants through an open and curious

Poems, metaphors, story-telling, and imagery can provide alternative tools for understanding mindfulness

stance, communicating possibility and choice, while allowing the participants to come to their own conclusion about the poem, story, or metaphor presented. Research has found that the more information is personally meaningful and more organized into a coherent whole, the better it is retained and generalized; poems, metaphors, stories, and imagery facilitate this coherence (Otto, 2000).

Poetry is a poignant way to awaken and access experiences on a felt, embodied level (Fox, 1997). When a person hears a poem, he or she may experience a resonance with his or her own stories in a way that has never been verbalized (Carroll, 2005). Furthermore, poetry has long illuminated individuals' relationship with a universal humanity: taking a listener from the isolation of *me* or *I* to a greater community of humanity; opening the window to a wider, broader perspective of life's difficulties.

Standalone metaphors and short fables also provide a springboard to wider application of learning. Metaphors tend to celebrate the paradoxical aspects of being human and the processes of mindfulness. They allow the impossible and represent the possibility of change and metamorphosis. Metaphors and fables are also often easily remembered and generalized from the environment in which they were learned to an individual's own contextual environment, which is useful for broad-based behavior change (Hayes et al., 2012).

Using imagery during mindfulness interventions may also accelerate learning. Imagery engages all of the senses via imaginal processes, and has the capacity to deliver multiple layers of complex, encoded messages by way of simple symbols and metaphors. By bypassing the thinking mind and connecting at a more emotional and visceral level, altered and broader perspective may safely emerge. This somatic delivery is powerful and can transform the ways in which people think, feel, and, ultimately, act. Like mindfulness, poetry, metaphors, storytelling, and imagery do not try to *fix*. Instead, they act as a reflection. These teaching modalities can provide greater perspective and offer a path toward novel, nonthreatening insights and understandings of one's own condition.

4.4　　Formal and Informal Mindfulness Practices

4.4.1　　Formal Mindfulness Practices

The practice of mindfulness can take many forms including formal and informal practices. Formal practices create opportunities to experience mindfulness at its deepest levels and include concentration practices, as well as open monitoring practices. Formal mindfulness meditations are considered formal because they are typically practiced by setting aside and dedicating a period of time in one's day to engage in the practice. The *body scan meditation* (see an example in Appendix 2) is often the first formal practice introduced in an MBI. It is a somatically-oriented, attention-focusing practice designed to increase interoceptive awareness and acceptance (Dreeben et al., 2013). During this practice, participants are invited to lie on their backs, or to sit comfortably in a chair, with their eyes closed, open, or half-open with a soft gaze. Participants successively focus attention on areas of the body, often beginning with the

Formal mindfulness practice involves dedicating a period of time in one's day to engage in one or more mindfulness practices

toes of one foot and moving slowly up the leg, then slowly through the other leg, torso, arms, neck, and head. Participants are instructed to notice the sensations that are present in that area with an attitude of openness and curiosity: releasing any intent to change the sensations. Participants are asked to gently notice when the mind wanders, and then kindly return attention to the bodily sensations, without self-criticism or blame.

The body scan meditation develops several important skills, including concentration and attentional flexibility. It can also enhance the felt sense of being localized within one's physical body, and cultivates a subtle distinction between thinking about the body and perceiving the body (Mehling et al., 2012). Furthermore, during the body scan meditation, one begins to notice the transitory nature of experience, as well as the frequency and automaticity of judgmental and narrative thinking (Carmody & Baer, 2008; Dreeben et al., 2013).

Mindful breathing is a second common formal practice. During this practice, participants sit upright on a chair or on a cushion in an alert and relaxed position. Eyes can be closed or softly gazing downward. Participants are guided to become aware of physical sensations – especially those associated with the process of breathing – and to observe them without the intention of altering them. Participants are asked to notice in an accepting, nonjudgmental manner when their minds wander to something other than the breath, and to gently return focus to the sensations of breathing. Mindful breathing may strengthen attention allocation, enhance an individual's ability to recognize the transient nature of experiences, and is associated with decreased physiological arousal, stress reactivity, and emotional reactivity (Delizonna, Williams, & Langer, 2009; Feldman, Greeson, & Senville, 2010).

Sitting meditation is a third formal practice taught in many MBIs (see an example in Appendix 3). Participants are typically instructed to sit on a chair or a meditation cushion in a comfortable posture that is both alert and relaxed. Eyes can be closed or softly gazing downward. First, participants direct their attention to the sensations and movements of breathing. When the mind wanders off, they gently return their attention to breathing. After several minutes, the focus of attention is shifted to other bodily sensations. Participants are instructed to notice these nonjudgmentally and with acceptance as best they can, bringing an attitude of interest and curiosity to both pleasant and unpleasant sensations. A sitting meditation may also include a period of listening mindfully to sounds in the environment, noticing the tone, quality, volume, and duration of the sounds and to observe periods of silence between sounds, with the intention to refrain from judging, analyzing, or pairing sounds with cognitive narratives. Next, the facilitator might guide participants to shift the focus of attention to thoughts. Participants are instructed to observe the thoughts as temporary events that come and go in their field of awareness, and to note thought content briefly without reacting, interacting, or becoming absorbed in the content. Participants also practice observing emotions in a similar fashion, briefly noting the type of emotion they are experiencing (e.g., anxiety, sadness, irritability), locating the physical sensations of the emotion, and labeling any thoughts associated with the emotion. In a more advanced practice, a sitting meditation may end with a period of *choiceless awareness*, in which participants notice anything that enters their field of awareness (e.g., bodily sensations, thoughts, emotions, sounds, urges) as they naturally arise. This choiceless awareness is likened to the presence of mind that is *wide awake*, and is described as a relaxed receptivity characterized by silently observing without interacting. The sitting meditation practice enables one to clearly observe the building up of reactions and secondary appraisals to simple sensations, emotions, or thoughts. A sitting meditation also strengthens one's ability to simultaneously maintain this relaxed nonreactive receptivity while engaging in everyday life with all of the internal and external stimuli and stressors that arises (Anālayo, 2004).

Walking meditation is another formal practice frequently taught in MBIs. During a walking meditation, the gaze is generally soft and straight ahead. One option for the practice is to have approximately 80% of the attention directed inward, while the remaining 20% is directed outward towards the external environment. Attention is directed to the sensations of movements, shifts of weight and balance, and perceptions in the feet and legs associated with walking. As in other meditation exercises, participants are encouraged to notice when their minds wander off and gently to bring their attention back to the physical sensations of walking. Walking meditation often is practiced slowly. To emphasize the absence of a destination, participants typically walk back and forth across a room; however, a mindful walking practice can also occur outside. When practiced outside, the participant might be instructed to be open and receptive to all five senses; curiously exploring the surroundings through the sensory perceptions of sight, sounds, smell, touch, and movement.

Although several formal mindfulness practices involve a posture of stillness, formal practice can also involve movement

Mindful movement or mindful stretching is another formal mindfulness practice. Mindful movement often involves engaging in gentle and slow stretches or postures while focusing one's awareness on body sensations that arise from moment to moment. In addition, while stretching or holding postures, the participant practices noticing any thoughts and emotions that arise with an attitude of openness and curiosity. Mindful movement can be practiced standing, lying down, or in a chair.

Finally, *loving kindness meditation* (LKM) is based on a Buddhist practice that is becoming more commonly employed in MBIs. Loving kindness (*metta*) refers to a mental state of unselfish and unconditional kindness to all beings (Hofmann, Grossman, & Hinton, 2011). LKM incorporates elements of both concentration and open monitoring practices and is designed to increase feelings of social connection and compassion for one's self and others. Participants focus on developing love and compassion first for themselves, and then gradually extend this loving kindness to ever more *unlikeable* others, progressing from self to a friend, to someone one does not know, to someone one does not like, to all living beings (Salzberg, 2011). The sequence of the foci of LKM can be altered to cultivate self-compassion. The practice may start by asking the participants to first visualize a beloved person or pet and invite the participants to send the wishes of goodwill to this loved one, to whom it is often easy to offer such wishes. Next, participants are asked to include a more difficult person in the circle of good will, repeating the phrases as "May he live in safety. May he be happy. May he be healthy in body and mind." This can often be more challenging. Finally, participants are asked to release the image of the loved one or others and turn the loving kindness and goodwill towards one's self and while repeating the phrases, "May I live in safety. May I be happy. May I be healthy in body and mind," to practice relating to the self in a more compassionate and generous manner.

4.4.2   Informal Mindfulness Practices

Informal practices refer to the engagement of mindful awareness during daily activities and complement the meditative awareness cultivated in formal practices. The raisin exercise and SOBER breathing space, as discussed in Chapter 2, are examples of informal mindfulness practices, and the raisin exercise illustrates that by simply changing the quality of attention during daily activities, one can significantly change the nature of the experience. Participants are encouraged to apply mindful awareness to routine activities, such as washing the dishes, cleaning the house, eating, driving, and shopping. Increased awareness of daily experiences is believed to lead to increased self-awareness and enhanced the ability to make real-time, adaptive decisions during difficult and problematic situations as they arise. Furthermore, applying mindfulness to daily living can increase the frequency and enjoyment of pleasant moments.

Informal mindfulness practice involves applying mindfulness to daily activities or situations

Mindfulness of breathing in daily life also is encouraged and promotes the generalization of self-awareness of the constantly fluctuating internal states experienced in ordinary activities. Turning one's attention to one's breathing at any moment of the day is intended to increase self-awareness, develop insight and familiarity to the nature of the mind, and reduces habitual, automatic, and maladaptive behaviors (Feldman et al., 2010).

Walking meditation can similarly be incorporated into daily life, such as while running errands or walking between the car and the workplace. For individuals with an increased sense of anxiety when sitting quietly or those with a very active minds, mindful movement and walking meditations can be a valuable introduction to mindfulness practice.

4.5   Participant Considerations

4.5.1   Participant Willingness

Participants may be hesitant or unwilling to engage in mindfulness practice for a variety of reasons. The previously discussed approach of rolling with resistance, describes an approach in which a facilitator avoids direct argument or conflict with participants, and instead focuses on a collaborative, nonjudgmental, and curious approach. When participants express unwillingness to practice mindfulness, it may be tempting to launch into a lecture about mindfulness and attempt to convince them that mindfulness is worth practicing. However, this type of persuasion can elicit *push back*, it can be exhausting and frustrating for the facilitator, and it ultimately is likely to be ineffective.

As a general guideline, providing simple reflective statements that validate participant concerns and experiences can be a helpful first step. Participants may simply be unfamiliar with mindfulness practice, and may doubt whether they are able to engage, or may question whether it can be helpful for them.

In these cases, it can be effective to first validate participant concerns, and then ask if a participant is willing to give it a try. For example, "so this sounds a little weird to you, and you're not sure how it could help you. I wonder if you'd be willing to give it a try, as long as you're already here, and just see what happens."

In other cases, participants may have specific reasons, such as religious or cultural, for not wanting to engage in mindfulness practices. They may have concerns about how mindfulness practice fits in with, or is counter or threatening to, their own religious beliefs and practices. It is important to be attentive and sensitive to these concerns, rather than defaulting to assumptions based on limited information such as appearance or race/ethnicity of a participant. In may be helpful to provide background about the history and context of the practices used in MBIs, asking participants for permission to share with them more information that might be helpful for them to know. For example, "Would it be alright with you if I shared a little more information about mindfulness that is related to your concerns about mindfulness being a religion?"

It can be helpful to provide basic information about mindfulness and its historical background

The facilitator may share how mindfulness is taught by a wide variety of healthcare professionals and in many different settings, religions and cultures, to individuals with all sorts of backgrounds and beliefs. Ultimately, of course, the participants' choices need to be honored, and these practices may not be aligned with their own beliefs or values.

Participants may also have difficulties initiating or adhering to regular mindfulness practice outside of sessions. Similarly, it is important to avoid attempting to persuade participants of the benefits of mindfulness to motivate them to practice. While facilitators may recognize the potential benefits, *attempts to persuade tend to be both ineffective and counter to the spirit of MBI approaches*. Rather, facilitators might reflect the resistance or difficulties, and engage in a collaborative discussion, eliciting ideas and experiences from participants about the rationale for practicing mindfulness, based on participants' presenting concerns and goals.

At times, there may be directly addressable barriers preventing an individual from engaging in out of session practice. The facilitator might gently ask the participant about what he or she thinks is getting in the way and may also review the *five hindrances* (i.e., barriers to mindfulness practice): craving, aversion, sleepiness, restlessness, and doubt. Examples of other logistic barriers that can come up are difficulty finding a time or place to practice, being too busy, lack of planning, or difficulty finding and playing guided recordings. After identifying key barriers with the participants, the facilitator might proceed to collaborate with the participants to jointly develop a plan to address the logistic barriers, while also modeling acceptance and universality of the hindrances. Participants may need more information or a review about different ways of practicing mindfulness (e.g., formal and informal practices). Finally, it can be helpful to emphasize that there is not one way to practice mindfulness, and that what is most important is for individuals to find a way to personalize their practice and make it sustainable in their lives.

4.5.2   Adapting Mindfulness-Based Approaches to Meet Participant Needs

There are circumstances in which delivery of current standard formats of mindfulness-based approaches require adaptation to suit the specific and unique needs, characteristics, and experiences of participants. For example, participants with certain physical conditions may have difficulties sitting for long periods of time, or practicing in certain positions. Therefore, providing a range of postures and formats for practice can make this approach accessible to a wider range of individuals. Another consideration is participants (e.g., children and adolescents, adult participants with severe psychopathology and cognitive impairments) who may have difficulty with longer meditations, and for whom shorter mindfulness practices may be preferable and more appropriate. The facilitator may also consider matching the style of language to the cognitive and learning abilities of participants. For some participants, words such as "reactive" or "decentering" may be confusing, and simpler language may be necessary when leading meditations and discussions. Some MBIs include practices that involve elements of imaginal exposure in which participants are instructed to imagine a difficult or challenging situation while practicing mindfulness skills. For example, in mindfulness-based relapse prevention (MBRP), the urge surfing practice involves imagining a triggering situation. For such practices, it is important to consider the readiness of the participant, the current severity of symptoms, and the stage of treatment. Imaginal exposure exercises can be adapted depending on these factors. For example, for participants early in substance abuse treatment, the facilitator might initially conduct imaginal exposure practices with less triggering situations, such as minor interpersonal conflicts or daily hassles.

Working with participants who have been exposed to trauma can be particularly challenging. For example, participants with trauma histories may not feel safe closing their eyes or lying on the floor. While helpful and appropriate in some populations, these are not critical elements of the practice. Practicing with eyes open and downcast, or in a seated or standing position may be more comfortable for some participants. It is also important to realize that participants with trauma exposure may experience triggers when focusing on their body or breath. In these cases, the facilitator might consider starting with an alternative primary focus, for example sounds, sights, or activities such as eating or walking. It can also be helpful to take a gradual or stepped approach to introducing mindfulness practices (e.g., starting with informal or shorter practices, and building up to longer, formal practices).

Another consideration when implementing and disseminating MBIs is culture and context. While MBIs are still relatively new in the treatment field, such adaptations are still in early developmental stages. To best serve ethnically and culturally diverse populations, preliminary efforts have been made to adapt mindfulness-based approaches. For example, Hinton, Pich, Hofmann, & Otto (2013) describe culturally adapted cognitive behavioral therapy, which involves mindfulness techniques adapted for ethnic minority populations and traumatized refugees. Similarly, Sobczak & West (2011) provide several recommendations for delivering mindfulness-based therapies to participants from underserved backgrounds. For example, they emphasize that these participants often experience an increased number of environmental stressors (e.g., pov-

Although MBIs include common components and methods, the delivery needs to meet the unique needs of each participant

erty, discrimination) and face considerable adversity. Accordingly, introducing or discussing the concept of opening to and tolerating difficult emotions in the context of mindfulness practice may come across as insensitive, invalidating, or unreasonable. It may therefore be skillful to validate stressors faced by these participants, and acknowledge that avoiding emotions may indeed be useful and adaptive in some situations; however, this approach may not serve us well in other ways. Overall, research to date suggests that mindfulness-based approaches are acceptable and effective among ethnic and cultural minority populations (Fuchs, Lee, Roemer, & Orsillo, 2013; Witkiewitz, Greenfield, & Bowen, 2013). However, more research is needed to understand how mindfulness-based approaches can most sensitively and effectively be applied to ethnic and cultural minorities and underserved populations.

Preliminary research indicates that MBIs are effective among ethnic and cultural minority populations

4.5.3   Contraindications

While studies across diverse settings and samples have shown evidence of feasibility, acceptability, and efficacy, there are population- and context-specific considerations to consider when developing and implementing MBIs. In a review of potential risks and adverse effects of participation in MBIs and related meditation-intensive programs, Lustyk and colleagues (2009) highlight mental, physical, and spiritual health as primary categories of risk and offer suggestions to minimize each of these. Fully informed consent and screening of participants are essential to each of these concerns, as is facilitators' training in delivery and established practice of mindfulness meditation.

To minimize risk of adverse mental and physical health events, Lustyk and colleagues (2009) recommend screening for suicidality and active psychosis and emphasize the need for presence of, or access to, a mental health professional during the MBI course. It is also advisable for MBI facilitators to ensure participants have a primary mental and physical health provider during participation in the group.

Although MBIs are typically secularized, as mindfulness practice does not inherently include religious doctrine or requirement of any belief system, the practices are undeniably of Buddhist origin. Evidence suggests that participation in intensive Vipassana or mindfulness meditation does not change nor lessen beliefs in other religions (Bowen, Bergman, & Witkiewitz, 2015). However, it is critical for researchers and clinicians to be aware of, and sensitive to, these roots when working with populations who may hold beliefs from different religions and be prepared to address any concerns that arise.

Consideration of and experience with specific risk factors is critical in any intervention, and it is imperative to attend to risk through screening, safety procedures, and thorough clinician training. However, studies reviewed here, among multiple others, provide evidence for acceptability and benefit for MBIs specifically adapted for high risk populations, such as individuals with posttraumatic stress disorder (PTSD), severe substance use disorders, and borderline personality disorder, when facilitators are properly trained and precautions are taken to ensure participant safety.

4.6   Structural Adaptations for Delivering Mindfulness-Based Interventions

4.6.1   Closed Group Format

Mindfulness-based group therapies and programs are often delivered in closed cohort formats, with the same group of individuals attending each successive session, and no new individuals joining the group after the first session. Most MBIs described in the research literature have used closed groups, and thus most empirical support for MBIs are based on the closed group format.

The primary benefits of the closed group format include gradual and stepped introduction of new material that is conceptually grounded in practices from the previous sessions. Many MBIs begin with the raisin exercise. Participants are instructed to bring a curious attention to a tangible, external object. Practices then follow a succession, from the body scan, which provides a focus on the physical sensations of the body, to mindfulness of more subtle sensations of the breath, and later progresses to observation of less tangible points of focus, such as emotions and thoughts. Another benefit of the closed group format is the continuity of members in attendance, which can provide a consistent platform for forming social networks and building social support.

Most empirical research to date has evaluated mindfulness groups delivered in a closed group format

4.6.2   Rolling Group Format

For many treatment settings, closed groups may present logistical challenges. It may be difficult to recruit a sufficient number of participants at one time to start a group, and may not be realistic or beneficial for participants to wait to begin the program until the next group begins. In such cases, an open or *rolling* group in which both newcomers and prior attendees may attend any given session may be more realistic,. Although there is limited research on rolling MBI groups, MBIs have been successfully delivered in this format. We have designed a protocol for a rolling mindfulness-based relapse prevention (MBRP) group, and it is currently being implemented at a residential substance abuse treatment facility. Below we describe general considerations for designing and delivering a rolling mindfulness group, including group size, length and frequency of sessions, session content, and balancing the needs of both returning and new participants.

The delivery of mindfulness groups in an open or *rolling* format may be preferable in various real-world treatment settings

In determining the overall design of a rolling group, considerations include the target population, setting, and specific treatment targets of the mindfulness-based intervention. Our goal was to adapt MBRP, a treatment with eight 2-hour sessions, to a residential substance abuse treatment setting in which most participants attended three to four weeks of treatment. We designed seven unique 90-minute modules, with two modules per week, with each module on a separate day. This design allowed us to retain a substantial amount of the content of the standard eight-session MBRP, and provided the majority of participants at the residential center an opportunity to attend all seven modules during a single treatment stay.

One of the major challenges of leading a rolling group is simultaneously balancing the needs of newcomers and regulator attendees. In any given session, some participants may be entirely new to the group and to mindfulness practice, while others may have attended multiple sessions. It is helpful to include introductory components in each session to orient newcomers, as well as new components to keep previous attendees engaged. In the rolling MBRP group, we provide a brief introduction of the group and review the group rules (e.g., confidentiality, respect for others, etc.) at the beginning of every session to orient newcomers. Each session then includes the same instructions for a standard mindfulness practice, comprised of a brief check-in that invites participants to notice their present experience (body sensations, thoughts, and emotions) and share briefly one or two aspects that they notice. They are then guided through a brief mindful breathing practice. Beginning with the same practice at every session helps create consistency and structure across the different sessions. The mindful check-in and beginning practice also serve to introduce newcomers to two key processes that are emphasized throughout the group: observing one's own internal experience and redirecting one's attention to the breath. At every session, facilitators conduct inquiry following the beginning practice, which can orient newcomers to the practice of inquiry, and model the process of sharing their experience of the practice. Newcomers to a rolling group are also oriented to the intentions and content of the program through a brief review of key concepts that have been discussed in prior sessions. For example, following the beginning mindfulness practice and inquiry, the facilitator may pose one or two questions to prior attendees to review basic points from prior sessions. Participants might review their understanding and experience of mindfulness, or simply share what they have learned or observed about their experience thus far in the group. Prior attendees often share ways in which mindfulness practice has been helpful to them. These comments can enhance interest and motivation of newcomers.

For rolling groups, it can be helpful to keep things simple and focus on a smaller range of material. Attempting to cover too much material can be counterproductive and especially difficult in a context in which new participants may be present at each group. In the rolling MBRP rolling group, for example, we use a *less is more* model, and review and practice the *SOBER space* every other session. Similar to the beginning mindful check-in and brief practice, the repetition of the SOBER creates a sense of structure and consistency across the groups.

It is helpful to include new material in each session to keep prior attendees engaged. Thus, in addition to these repeated components, new concepts and practices are introduced, and each module generally centers on a new theme (e.g., mindfulness in high-risk situations, stepping out of autopilot). In our experience, participants are able to quickly orient themselves to the group and easily catch up to others.

4.6.3   Residential Treatment Settings

Empirical studies have demonstrated that MBIs are feasible and effective in residential treatment settings (Bowen et al., 2006; Witkiewitz, Warner, et al., 2014). Didonna (2009) provides a helpful overview of potential adaptions to

MBI protocols for residential settings. He reviews several specific challenges that can arise during a group, such as participants falling asleep (potentially due to the side effects of medications), emotional arousal, distracting noises and commotion in the background, participants arriving late to groups, or leaving the group early, difficulties sitting for long periods of time due to physical conditions, and difficulty staying engaged and thus causing disruptions (potentially due to cognitive impairments, emotional arousal, or other acute symptoms). Didonna (2009) offers recommendations for managing these common challenges, including: (1) a cofacilitation model in which two therapists conduct each session, (2) limiting group size when working with participants with severe conditions, (3) excluding participants who will be too disruptive, (4) asking participants to leave the group when they become too disruptive or dysregulated and escorting them back to their room, (5) providing more thorough verbal instruction during guided meditations, (6) seating difficult or unstable participants closer to the facilitator, (6) not permitting participants to enter the group late, (7) using background music, (8) progressing from brief and informal practice at the beginning of the program to longer and formal practices in later weeks, (9) carefully selecting practices which are not too activating for highly dysregulated participants, (10) waking up participants if they fall asleep, (11) capitalizing on difficulties (e.g., noise disruptions) by emphasizing that these are opportunities to practice openness and nonjudgment, and (12) encouraging and supporting mindfulness practice between group sessions.

> Research has documented that MBIs are effective when delivered in residential treatment settings

4.6.4   Individual Format

For therapists in private practice, the opportunities for group therapy may be limited. We have found that mindfulness-based approaches can be adapted for individual therapy with minimal modifications. For example, an individual therapist may encourage specific practices that are specifically helpful for a particular participant, refer a participant to attend a mindfulness group (e.g., MBSR) as an adjunct to individual therapy, or incorporate specific components or modules within manualized treatments to address certain issues and symptoms. The ability to integrate mindfulness practice and training into individual therapy in a flexible and skillful manner requires an understanding of the many forms of mindfulness practices, the intentions behind these practices, ways of applying practice in daily life, and ways in which different practices may be more or less useful and appropriate for certain issues and types of participants. Pollak, Pedualla, and Siegel (2014) have described mindfulness-based psychotherapy with individual participants, and we refer interested readers to that resource for more information about incorporating MBIs in the context of individual treatment.

> MBI components or modules from manuals for groups can be flexibly incorporated into individual psychotherapy

Few empirical studies have examined the efficacy of the manualized MBIs conducted in individual versus group format. However, one study (Tovote et al., 2014) comparing individual MBCT to cognitive-behavioral treatment for depression among patients with diabetes found no significant differences between the two treatment formats, with both more effective than a wait-list control condition in reducing depression symptoms and distress.

4.7   MBIs Training and Supervision

A fundamental preparatory step for providing MBIs with fidelity is MBI facilitation training and adequate supervision. Training begins with a committed, regular personal mindfulness practice. Developers of the primary MBIs have described the training required for delivering the programs. For example, to facilitate mindfulness-based cognitive therapy (MBCT), the requirements include: (1) accreditation as a counselor, psychotherapist, or other mental health professional; (2) training in delivery of cognitive-behavioral therapy; (3) experience in leading group psychotherapy interventions; (4) training in MBCT via an intensive week-long teacher training; and (5) an established commitment to ongoing personal meditation practice. These five criteria are common for many of the MBIs described in this book.

Developing effective training and supervision models for mindfulness-based interventions is a growing area of interest

Established models and recommendations for MBI facilitator training and supervision incorporate elements characteristic of the mindfulness-based approach. Trainings in MBIs are typically experientially based, allowing the trainee to experience firsthand the practices and explorations at the heart of the program. The qualities that are fostered in mindfulness practice, including openness, awareness, nonjudgment, and curiosity, are central to the MBI training and supervision processes as well.

Evans and colleagues (2015) describe MBI facilitator supervision as encompassing teaching, group facilitation, theoretical understanding, and personal practice. Supervision sessions are present moment focused, and the supervisor models curiosity and nonjudgmental awareness during supervision sessions. Supervision might also begin with a mindfulness practice to encourage present moment awareness during the supervision session. Similar to facilitating MBI groups with participants, the intention of supervision is to teach additional elements through modeling, including exhibiting self-compassion, compassion toward others, and genuine curiosity for present-moment experience. Supervisors of MBIs are also expected to have an established commitment to ongoing personal meditation practice.

4.8   Efficacy of MBIs and Related Approaches

4.8.1   Mindfulness-Based Stress Reduction (MBSR)

Although MBSR was originally studied among individuals with chronic pain, it is now used with a wide range of stress-related conditions

There is a growing body of evidence from randomized clinical trials (RCTs) demonstrating the effectiveness of MBSR in improving a range of physical and psychological outcomes in comparison to control conditions. Outcome studies of MBSR have demonstrated efficacy in improving symptoms associated with a wide variety of stress-related illnesses, including depression and anxiety (Hofmann et al., 2010), and have been shown to inhibit unhealthy adaptations or coping responses to chronic stress, such as smoking, decreased exercise, and poor sleep (Gross et al., 2011). Recent reviews have summarized the evidence of the efficacy of MBSR for persons with cancer (Shennan, Payne, & Fenlon, 2011), chronic pain (Greeson & Eisenlohr-Moul, 2014), and chronic medical conditions (Bohlmeijer, Prenger, Taal, & Cuijpers, 2010).

MBSR has also been shown to improve the biomarkers of glycemic control in diabetes (Gregg, Callaghan, Hayes, & Glenn-Lawson, 2007; Rosenzweig et al., 2007), enhance immune response (Davidson et al., 2003), and accelerate skin healing in psoriasis (Kabat-Zinn et al., 1998). Furthermore, trials of MBSR with health providers and community samples demonstrate significant improvements in stress management and enhanced well-being (Irving et al., 2012; Shapiro, Thakur, & de Sousa, 2014). Adaptations to MBSR have been made for teens (MBSR-Teen) and RCTs demonstrated greater improvements in anxiety, depression, somatic distress, sleep quality, and self-esteem when compared to a treatment as usual group (Biegel, Brown, Shapiro, & Schubert, 2009). Finally, MBSR has recently been adapted for first responders, such as police officers, (mindfulness-based resilience training; MBRT), with open trials evincing promising results (Christopher et al., 2015).

4.8.2   Mindfulness-Based Cognitive Therapy (MBCT)

Results of a meta-analysis indicated that MBCT has been shown to nearly halve the risk of relapse among individuals with a history of at least three prior episodes of depression who are currently in remission (Piet & Hougaard, 2011) and is comparable to the use of an antidepressant in preventing recurrence (Segal et al., 2010). Although there are potential practical and theoretical drawbacks to using MBCT in currently depressed populations, randomized controlled data suggest it may be as effective in currently depressed patients as those in remission and similar in efficacy to CBT (White, 2015). Furthermore, recent research suggests MBCT may be effective for individuals with bipolar disorder; however, to date, there are no RCTs to confirm the effectiveness for this population (Ives-Deliperi, Howells, Stein, Meintjes, & Horn, 2013).

MBCT is effective is reducing the risk of relapse among individuals with at least three prior episodes of depression

4.8.3   Mindfulness-Based Relapse Prevention (MBRP)

Although youngest of the mindfulness-based programs discussed thus far, empirical evidence to support the efficacy of MBRP is growing. In the first randomized trial of MBRP, Bowen and colleagues (2009) compared MBRP to treatment-as-usual (TAU; 12-step and psychoeducation components) among individuals with substance use disorders who had completed intensive outpatient or inpatient treatment. Results demonstrated that MBRP produced better substance use outcomes than TAU during treatment and over 4 months following the intervention. More recently, Bowen et al. (2014) compared MBRP to both TAU and cognitive-behavioral relapse prevention (RP). Both RP and MBRP were more effective at reducing prevalence and severity of relapse than TAU at the 6-month post-intervention follow-up. At 12-month follow-up, compared to both RP and TAU, MBRP participants had fewer substance use days and an increased rate of abstaining from heavy drinking. In a similar trial, Witkiewitz, Warner, et al. (2014) compared MBRP to RP in a residential treatment program for women involved in the criminal justice system. Results indicated that receiving MBRP, as compared to RP, resulted in significantly fewer drug use days and fewer legal and medical problems at the 15-month

Studies show MBRP
is effective when
delivered as a group-
based aftercare
intervention for
substance use
disorder

post-intervention follow-up. Although findings suggest a mindfulness-based approach may confer advantages over standard relapse prevention approaches for substance use disorders, the overall body of literature on MBRP is still small and future studies are warranted. In particular, there are few empirical data suggesting MBRP is efficacious as a primary stand-alone treatment or when delivered as an individual, rather than group-based, intervention.

4.8.4   Mindfulness-Based Cancer Recovery (MBCR)

In the largest randomized controlled trial of MBCR to date, Carlson and her colleagues (2013) compared MBCR to supportive expressive group therapy, an active intervention with prior empirical support, and a one-day stress management control group. Distressed survivors of breast cancer who received MBCR showed greater improvements in stress symptoms immediately after the intervention, but not depressed mood, compared to both supportive expressive group and the control group. Of note, there have also been earlier studies of MBCR in which the intervention was referred to as MBSR. Piet, Würtzen, & Zachariae (2012) conducted a meta-analysis of 22 studies on mindfulness-based therapies for adult cancer patients. Overall, they found moderate average effect sizes across studies in reducing anxiety and depression symptoms. The authors concluded that there is support for the use of mindfulness-based therapies for cancer patients with anxiety and depression symptoms. Future work is needed to compare the relative efficacy of MBCR compared to other empirically supported interventions among cancer patients and survivors.

4.8.5   Mindfulness-Based Eating Awareness Training (MB-EAT)

Kristeller et al. (2013) compared MB-EAT to a psychoeducational/cognitive behavioral intervention and a waitlist control for binge eating disorder. Results demonstrated that both MB-EAT and the cognitive behavioral intervention produced greater improvements in number of binge days, binge eating severity, and depression than the control group at the 1- and 4-month post-intervention follow-up, although there were no significant differences between MB-EAT and the cognitive behavioral intervention on these outcomes. Among individuals still binge eating during the 4-month follow-up period, however, those who had received MB-EAT had significantly smaller sized binges compared to those in both the cognitive behavioral and the control conditions. In addition to MB-EAT, there have been numerous studies examining other similar MBIs for binge eating. Results of a meta-analysis (Godfrey, Gallo, & Afari, 2015) demonstrated that there were generally moderate to large effects of these interventions on binge eating, suggesting that MBIs may be a promising approach for treating binge eating disorder. However, there is not yet clear evidence that mindfulness-based approaches are efficacious for anorexia nervosa or bulimia nervosa.

4.8.6   Mindfulness-Based Therapy for Insomnia (MBTI)

Ong and colleagues (2014) compared MBTI to standard MBSR and to an 8-week self-monitoring control group for treatment of chronic insomnia. Compared to the control group, both MBTI and MBSR produced better outcomes at post-treatment in total wake time, pre-sleep arousal, and insomnia severity. There were no differences in outcomes between MBTI and MBSR immediately post-treatment; however, MBTI produced significantly greater improvements in insomnia severity over the 6-month follow-up period compared to both MBSR and the control group. These findings suggest that MBTI is a promising treatment for insomnia. However, the empirical literature on MBTI is still relatively small, and future research will further our understanding of how MBTI compares to other treatment options.

4.8.7   Efficacy of Related Approaches

Dialetical Behavior Therapy

Meta-analytic studies suggest strong empirical support for DBT in treatment of BPD, especially in reducing suicidal and self-injurious behavior (Kliem, Kröger, & Kosfelder, 2010; Panos, Jackson, Hasan, & Panos, 2013). Soler and colleagues (2012) recently investigated the specific role of mindfulness training in DBT. They examined effects of DBT mindfulness training as an adjunct to general psychiatric management for BPD. Results indicated that those who received the mindfulness training had significantly better improvements on behavioral measures of attention and impulsivity. Moreover, more time engaging in mindfulness practice was associated with greater reductions in psychiatric symptoms.

Metacognitive Therapy

Research demonstrates that MCT is effective in treating a wide spectrum of psychological disorders. A recent meta-analysis (Normann, Emmerik, & Morina, 2014) examined 16 studies, nine of which were RCTs. Results confirmed that MCT produced large within-group effect sizes for anxiety, depression, and metacognitions. Between groups results indicated that among individuals with anxiety and depression, compared to CBT, a large effect size was found in favor of MCT. Additionally, several RCTs have demonstrated MCT may be effective for treating PTSD and may exert larger and more rapid within group effect sizes than those associated with a prolonged exposure condition (Wells, Walton, Lovell, & Proctor, 2014). MCT has also recently been used with individuals experiencing psychosis, yielding promising results (Favrod et al., 2014), and within health psychology, specifically with cancer survivors (Cook et al., 2015).

> A recent meta-analysis demonstrated that MCT is an effective treatment for individuals with depression or an anxiety disorder

Acceptance and Commitment Therapy

There is a rapidly growing body of empirical studies on ACT for various mental health disorders and chronic health conditions. Several meta-analytic studies (Öst, 2008; Ruiz Jiménez, 2012; Veehof, Oskam, Schreurs, & Bohlmeijer, 2011) and reviews (Hayes et al., 2006; Pull, 2009) published in the past decade

Meta-analyses show that ACT is more effective than TAU and as effective as other interventions in treating many disorders

indicate that ACT appears to be more effective than treatment-as-usual and inactive control treatments, and equally as effective as other established therapies, in treating chronic pain, anxiety disorders, depression, and substance use disorders. To date, there does not appear to be clear evidence that ACT yields superior outcomes as compared to other established interventions, such as CBT, in treating any specific disorder. Research on mechanisms of change in ACT interventions is also gaining considerable ground. Altogether, these studies provide support for the position that ACT interventions influence key processes of change in the psychological flexibility model, such as acceptance, defusion, and values-consistent behavior, and that these processes are related to positive outcomes across a wide range of problems (Hayes et al., 2013).

5

Further Reading

Baer, R. A. (2015). *Mindfulness-based treatment approaches: Clinician's guide to evidence base and applications.* Cambridge, MA: Academic Press.
Thorough resource that includes a description of the session content and research for a variety of mindfulness-based interventions.

Brown, K. W., Creswell, J. D., & Ryan, R. M. (2015). *Handbook of mindfulness: Theory, research, and practice.* New York, NY: Guilford Press.
Edited volume that includes sections on the historical and theoretical background of mindfulness, treatment approaches, basic science investigations into mindfulness, and an examination of mindfulness for healthy populations.

Kabat-Zinn, J. (2013). *Full catastrophe living: Using the wisdom of the body and mind to face stress, pain, and illness* (Rev. ed.). New York, NY: Bantam.
Provides an overview of the approach used in mindfulness-based stress reduction. The original resource for the development of other MBSR-based mindfulness interventions.

Pollak, S. M., Pedulla, T., & Siegel, R. D. (2014). *Sitting together: Essential skills for mindfulness-based psychotherapy.* New York, NY: Guilford Press.
Step-by-step guidebook for bringing mindfulness into a psychoatherapy practice. Provides guidance for personal practice and leading mindfulness-based interventions.

Salzberg, S. (2011). *Real happiness: The power of meditation.* New York, NY: Workman Publishing Company.
Provides an overview of the basics of initiating and maintaining a daily mindfulness practice, as well as examining larger concepts of how meditation works and developing greater compassion and awareness through mindfulness practice.

6

References

Ahani, A., Wahbeh, H., Nezamfar, H., Miller, M., Erdogmus, D., & Oken, B. (2014). Quantitative change of EEG and respiration signals during mindfulness meditation. *Journal of NeuroEngineering and Rehabilitation, 11*(1), 87. http://doi.org/10.1186/1743-0003-11-87

Aldao, A., & Gross, J. J. (2015). Emotion regulation flexibility. *Cognitive Therapy and Research, 39*(3), 263–278. http://doi.org/10.1007/s10608-014-9662-4

Amaro, H., Spear, S., Vallejo, Z., Conron, K., & Black, D. S. (2014). Feasibility, acceptability, and preliminary outcomes of a mindfulness-based relapse prevention intervention for culturally-diverse, low-income women in substance use disorder treatment. *Substance Use & Misuse, 49*(5), 547–59.

Anālayo, B. (2004). *Sattipatthana: The direct path to realization*. Birmingham, UK: Windhorse Publications.

Ashworth, F., Gracey, F., & Gilbert, P. (2011). Compassion focused therapy after traumatic brain injury: Theoretical foundations and a case illustration. *Brain Impairment, 12*(2), 128–139. http://doi.org/10.1375/brim.12.2.128

Baer, R. A. (2003). Mindfulness training as a clinical intervention: A conceptual and empirical review. *Clinical Psychology: Science and Practice, 10*(2), 125–143. http://doi.org/10.1093/clipsy.bpg015

Baer, R. A. (2010). *Assessing mindfulness and acceptance processes in clients: Illuminating the theory and practice of change*. Oakland, CA: New Harbinger Publications.

Baer, R. A. (2015). Ethics, values, virtues, and character strengths in mindfulness-based interventions: A psychological science perspective. *Mindfulness, 6*, 956–969. http://doi.org/10.1007/s12671-015-0419-2

Baer, R. A., Smith, G. T., & Allen, K. B. (2004). Assessment of mindfulness by self-report: The Kentucky Inventory of Mindfulness Skills. *Assessment, 11*(3), 191–206. http://doi.org/10.1177/1073191104268029

Baer, R. A., Smith, G. T., Hopkins, J., Krietemeyer, J., & Toney, L. (2006). Using self-report assessment methods to explore facets of mindfulness. *Assessment, 13*(1), 27–45. http://doi.org/10.1177/1073191105283504

Banks, J. B., Welhaf, M. S., & Srour, A. (2015). The protective effects of brief mindfulness meditation training. *Consciousness and Cognition, 33*, 277–285. http://doi.org/10.1016/j.concog.2015.01.016

Bennett, H., & Wells, A. (2010). Metacognition, memory disorganization and rumination in posttraumatic stress symptoms. *Journal of Anxiety Disorders, 24*(3), 318–325. http://doi.org/10.1016/j.janxdis.2010.01.004

Benson, H., & Klipper, M. Z. (1976). *The relaxation response*. New York, NY: Avon Books.

Benson, H., Marzetta, B., Rosner, B., & Klemchuk, H. (1974). Decreased blood-pressure in pharmacologically treated hypertensive patients who regularly elicited the relaxation response. *The Lancet, 303*(7852), 289–291.

Biegel, G. M., Brown, K. W., Shapiro, S. L., & Schubert, C. M. (2009). Mindfulness-based stress reduction for the treatment of adolescent psychiatric outpatients: A randomized clinical trial. *Journal of Consulting and Clinical Psychology, 77*(5), 855. http://doi.org/10.1037/a0016241

Bieling, P. J., Hawley, L. L., Bloch, R. T., Corcoran, K. M., Levitan, R. D., Young, L. T., ... Segal, Z. V. (2012). Treatment-specific changes in decentering following mindfulness-based cognitive therapy versus antidepressant medication or placebo for prevention of depressive relapse. *Journal of Consulting and Clinical Psychology, 80*(3), 365–372.

Bishop, S. R., Lau, M., Shapiro, S., Carlson, L., Anderson, N. D., Carmody, J., … Velting, D. (2004). Mindfulness: A proposed operational definition. *Clinical Psychology: Science and Practice, 11*(3), 230–241. http://doi.org/10.1093/clipsy.bph077

Boccia, M., Piccardi, L., & Guariglia, P. (2015). The meditative mind: A comprehensive meta-analysis of MRI studies. *BioMed Research International, 2015*, 419808. http://doi.org/10.1155/2015/419808

Bodhi, B. (2005). *In the Buddha's words: An anthology from the Pali Canon.* Boston, MA: Wisdom Publications.

Bodhi, B. (2011). What does mindfulness really mean? A canonical perspective. *Contemporary Buddhism, 12*(1), 19–39. http://doi.org/10.1080/14639947.2011.564813

Bohlmeijer, E., Prenger, R., Taal, E., & Cuijpers, P. (2010). The effects of mindfulness-based stress reduction therapy on mental health of adults with a chronic medical disease: A meta-analysis. *Journal of Psychosomatic Research, 68*(6), 539–544. http://doi.org/10.1016/j.jpsychores.2009.10.005

Bohlmeijer, E., ten Klooster, P. M., Fledderus, M., Veehof, M., & Baer, R. (2011). Psychometric properties of the five facet mindfulness questionnaire in depressed adults and development of a short form. *Assessment, 18*(3), 308–20. http://doi.org/10.1177/1073191111408231

Bonanno, G. A., & Burton, C. L. (2013). Regulatory flexibility: An individual differences perspective on coping and emotion regulation. *Perspectives on Psychological Science, 8*(6), 591–612. http://doi.org/10.1177/1745691613504116

Bond, F. W., Hayes, S. C., Baer, R. A., Carpenter, K. M., Guenole, N., Orcutt, H. K., … Zettle, R. D. (2011). Preliminary psychometric properties of the Acceptance and Action Questionnaire–II: A revised measure of psychological inflexibility and experiential Avoidance. *Behavior Therapy, 42*(4), 676–688.

Bowen, S., Bergman, A., & Witkiewitz, K. (2015). Engagement in Buddhist meditation practices among non-Buddhists: Associations with religious identity and practice. *Mindfulness, 6*(6), 1456–1461.

Bowen, S., Chawla, N., Collins, S. E., Witkiewitz, K., Hsu, S., Grow, J., … Marlatt, A. (2009). Mindfulness-based relapse prevention for substance use disorders: A pilot efficacy trial. *Substance Abuse, 30*(4), 295–305. http://doi.org/10.1080/08897070903250084

Bowen, S., Chawla, N., & Marlatt, G. A. (2011). *Mindfulness-based relapse prevention for addictive behaviors: A clinician's guide.* New York, NY: Guilford Press.

Bowen, S., Witkiewitz, K., Clifasefi, S. L., Grow, J., Chawla, N., Hsu, S. H., … Larimer, M. E. (2014). Relative efficacy of mindfulness-based relapse prevention, standard relapse prevention, and treatment as usual for substance use disorders: A randomized clinical trial. *JAMA Psychiatry, 71*(5), 547–556.

Bowen, S., Witkiewitz, K., Dillworth, T. M., Chawla, N., Simpson, T. L., Ostafin, B. D., … Marlatt, G. A. (2006). Mindfulness meditation and substance use in an incarcerated population. *Psychology of Addictive Behaviors, 20*(3), 343–347. http://doi.org/10.1037/0893-164X.20.3.343

Braehler, C., Gumley, A., Harper, J., Wallace, S., Norrie, J., & Gilbert, P. (2013). Exploring change processes in compassion focused therapy in psychosis: Results of a feasibility randomized controlled trial. *British Journal of Clinical Psychology, 52*(2), 199–214.

Brewer, J. A., Elwafi, H. M., & Davis, J. H. (2013). Craving to quit: Psychological models and neurobiological mechanisms of mindfulness training as treatment for addictions. *Psychology of Addictive Behaviors, 27*(2), 366–379. http://doi.org/10.1037/a0028490

Brewer, J. A., Mallik, S., Babuscio, T. A., Nich, C., Johnson, H. E., Deleone, C. M., … Rounsaville, B. J. (2011). Mindfulness training for smoking cessation: Results from a randomized controlled trial. *Drug and Alcohol Dependence, 119*(1–2), 72–80. http://doi.org/10.1016/j.drugalcdep.2011.05.027

Brown, K. W., & Ryan, R. M. (2003). The benefits of being present: Mindfulness and its role in psychological well-being. *Journal of Personality and Social Psychology, 84*(4), 822–848. http://doi.org/10.1037/0022-3514.84.4.822

Brown, K. W., Ryan, R. M., & Creswell, J. D. (2007). Mindfulness: Theoretical foundations and evidence for its salutary effects. *Psychological Inquiry, 18*(4), 211–237. http://doi.org/10.1080/10478400701598298

Cardaciotto, L., Herbert, J. D., Forman, E. M., Moitra, E., & Farrow, V. (2008). The assessment of present-moment awareness and acceptance: The Philadelphia Mindfulness Scale. *Assessment, 15*(2), 204–223. http://doi.org/10.1177/1073191107311467

Carlson, L. E., & Speca, M. (2011). *Mindfulness-based cancer recovery: A step-by-step MBSR approach to help you cope with treatment and reclaim your life.* Oakland, CA: New Harbinger.

Carlson, L. E., Tamagawa, R., Speca, M., Faris, P., Doll, R., Stephen, J., & Drysdale, E. (2013). Randomized controlled trial of mindfulness-based cancer recovery versus supportive expressive group therapy for distressed survivors of breast cancer (MINDSET). *Journal of Clinical Oncology, 31*(25), 3119–3126.

Carmody, J., & Baer, R. A. (2008). Relationships between mindfulness practice and levels of mindfulness, medical and psychological symptoms and well-being in a mindfulness-based stress reduction program. *Journal of Behavioral Medicine, 31*(1), 23–33. http://doi.org/10.1007/s10865-007-9130-7

Carroll, R. (2005). Finding the words to say it: The healing power of poetry. *Evidence-Based Complementary and Alternative Medicine, 2*(2), 161–172. http://doi.org/10.1093/ecam/neh096

Carver, C. S., Scheier, M. F., & Weintraub, J. K. (1989). Assessing coping strategies: A theoretically based approach. *Journal of Personality and Social Psychology, 56*(2), 267–283. http://doi.org/10.1037/0022-3514.56.2.267

Chadwick, P., Hember, M., Symes, J., Peters, E., Kuipers, E., & Dagnan, D. (2008). Responding mindfully to unpleasant thoughts and images: Reliability and validity of the Southampton Mindfulness Questionnaire (SMQ). *The British Journal of Clinical Psychology, 47*(4), 451–455.

Chang, K.-M., Chen, S.-H., Lee, H.-Y., Ching, C. T.-S., & Huang, C.-L. (2012). A wireless accelerometer-based body posture stability detection system and its application for meditation practitioners. *Sensors, 12*(12), 17620–17632. http://doi.org/10.3390/s121217620

Chawla, N., & Ostafin, B. (2007). Experiential avoidance as a functional dimensional approach to psychopathology: An empirical review. *Journal of Clinical Psychology, 63*(9), 871–890. http://doi.org/10.1002/jclp.20400

Cheng, C., & Chan, M. S. (2014). Coping flexibility and psychological adjustment to stressful life changes: A meta-analytic review. *Psychological Bulletin, 140*(6), 1582–1607. http://doi.org/10.1037/a0037913

Chiesa, A., Anselmi, R., & Serretti, A. (2014). Psychological mechanisms of mindfulness-based interventions. *Holistic Nursing Practice, 28*(2), 124–148. http://doi.org/10.1097/HNP.0000000000000017

Chiesa, A., Calati, R., & Serretti, A. (2011). Does mindfulness training improve cognitive abilities? A systematic review of neuropsychological findings. *Clinical Psychology Review, 31*(3), 449–464. http://doi.org/10.1016/j.cpr.2010.11.003

Chiesa, A., & Serretti, A. (2011). Mindfulness based cognitive therapy for psychiatric disorders: A systematic review and meta-analysis. *Psychiatry Research, 187*(3), 441–453. http://doi.org/10.1016/j.psychres.2010.08.011

Christopher, M. S., Charoensuk, S., Gilbert, B. D., Neary, T. J., & Pearce, K. L. (2009). Mindfulness in Thailand and the United States: A case of apples versus oranges? *Journal of Clinical Psychology, 65*(6), 590–612.

Christopher, M. S., Goerling, R. J., Rogers, B. S., Hunsinger, M., Baron, G., Bergman, A. L., & Zava, D. T. (2015). A pilot study evaluating the effectiveness of a mindfulness-based intervention on cortisol awakening response and health outcomes among law enforcement officers. *Journal of Police and Criminal Psychology, 31*(1), 1–14.

Christopher, M. S., Woodrich, L. E., & Tiernan, K. A. (2014). Using cognitive interviews to assess the cultural validity of state and trait measures of mindfulness among Zen Buddhists. *Mindfulness, 5*(2), 145–160. http://doi.org/10.1007/s12671-012-0160-z

Cohen, J., Hansel, C. E., & Sylvester, J. D. (1956). Mind wandering. *British Journal of Psychology, 47*(1), 61–62. http://doi.org/10.1111/j.2044-8295.1956.tb00562.x

Conners, C. K. (1985). The computerized continuous performance test. *Psychopharmacology Bulletin, 21*(4), 891–892.

Cook, S. A., Salmon, P., Dunn, G., Holcombe, C., Cornford, P., & Fisher, P. (2015). A prospective study of the association of metacognitive beliefs and processes with persistent emotional distress after diagnosis of cancer. *Cognitive Therapy and Research, 39*(1), 51–60.

Crane, R. S., Stanley, S., Rooney, M., Bartley, T., Cooper, L., & Mardula, J. (2015). Disciplined improvisation: Characteristics of inquiry in mindfulness-based teaching. *Mindfulness, 6*(5), 1104–1114. http://doi.org/10.1007/s12671-014-0361-8

Dass, R., & Goleman, D. (1990). *Journey of awakening: A meditator's guidebook.* New York, NY: Bantam.

Davidson, R. J., Kabat-Zinn, J., Schumacher, J., Rosenkranz, M., Muller, D., Santorelli, S. F., … Sheridan, J. F. (2003). Alterations in brain and immune function produced by mindfulness meditation. *Psychosomatic Medicine, 65*(4), 564–570. http://doi.org/10.1097/01.PSY.0000077505.67574.E3

Davidson, R. J., & Kaszniak, A. W. (2015). Conceptual and methodological issues in research on mindfulness and meditation. *American Psychologist, 70*(7), 581–592. http://doi.org/10.1037/a0039512

Davis, K. M., Lau, M. A., & Cairns, D. R. (2009). Development and preliminary validation of a trait version of the Toronto Mindfulness Scale. *Journal of Cognitive Psychotherapy, 23*(3), 185–197. http://doi.org/10.1891/0889-8391.23.3.185

Delizonna, L. L., Williams, R. P., & Langer, E. J. (2009). The effect of mindfulness on heart rate control. *Journal of Adult Development, 16*(2), 61–65. http://doi.org/10.1007/s10804-009-9050-6

Desbordes, G., Gard, T., Hoge, E. A., Hölzel, B. K., Kerr, C., Lazar, S. W., … Vago, D. R. (2014). Moving beyond mindfulness: Defining equanimity as an outcome measure in meditation and contemplative research. *Mindfulness, 6*(2), 356–372. http://doi.org/10.1007/s12671-013-0269-8

Dhargyey, G. N. (1974). *Tibetan tradition of mental development: Oral teachings of Tibetan Lama.* Dharmasala, India: Library of Tibetan Works & Archives.

Didonna, F. (2009). Mindfulness-based interventions in an inpatient setting. In F. Didonna (Ed.), *Clinical Handbook of Mindfulness* (pp. 447–462). New York, NY: Springer.

Dreeben, S. J., Mamberg, M. H., & Salmon, P. (2013). The MBSR body scan in clinical practice. *Mindfulness, 4*(4), 394–401. http://doi.org/10.1007/s12671-013-0212-z

Epling, S. L., Russell, P. N., & Helton, W. S. (2015). A new semantic vigilance task: Vigilance decrement, workload, and sensitivity to dual-task costs. *Experimental Brain Research, 234*(1), 133–139. http://doi.org/10.1007/s00221-015-4444-0

Evans, A., Crane, R., Cooper, L., Mardula, J., Wilks, J., Surawy, C., Kenny, M. & Kuyken, W. (2015). A framework for supervision for mindfulness-based teachers: A space for embodied mutual inquiry. *Mindfulness, 6*(3), 572–581.

Favrod, J., Rexhaj, S., Bardy, S., Ferrari, P., Hayoz, C., Moritz, S., … Bonsack, C. (2014). Sustained antipsychotic effect of metacognitive training in psychosis: A randomized-controlled study. *European Psychiatry, 29*(5), 275–281. http://doi.org/10.1016/j.eurpsy.2013.08.003

Felder, J. N., Dimidjian, S., & Segal, Z. (2012). Collaboration in mindfulness-based cognitive therapy. *Journal of Clinical Psychology, 68*(2), 179–186. http://doi.org/10.1002/jclp.21832

Feldman, G., Greeson, J., & Senville, J. (2010). Differential effects of mindful breathing, progressive muscle relaxation, and loving-kindness meditation on decentering and negative reactions to repetitive thoughts. *Behaviour Research and Therapy, 48*(10), 1002–1011.

Feldman, G., Hayes, A., Kumar, S., Greeson, J., & Laurenceau, J.-P. (2007). Mindfulness and emotion regulation: The development and initial validation of the Cognitive and

Affective Mindfulness Scale-Revised (CMS-R). *Journal of Psychopathology and Behavioral Assessment, 29*(3), 177–190.

Fleming, S. M., & Lau, H. C. (2014). How to measure metacognition. *Frontiers in Human Neuroscience, 8*, 443. http://doi.org/10.3389/fnhum.2014.00443

Fox, J. J. (1997). *Poetic power of place: Comparative perspectives on Austronesian ideas of locality*. Canberra, Australia: ANU E Press.

Fox, K. C. R., Nijeboer, S., Dixon, M. L., Floman, J. L., Ellamil, M., Rumak, S. P., … Christoff, K. (2014). Is meditation associated with altered brain structure? A systematic review and meta-analysis of morphometric neuroimaging in meditation practitioners. *Neuroscience and Biobehavioral Reviews, 43*, 48–73.

Franklin, M. S., Broadway, J. M., Mrazek, M. D., Smallwood, J., & Schooler, J. W. (2013). Window to the wandering mind: Pupillometry of spontaneous thought while reading. *Quarterly Journal of Experimental Psychology, 66*(12), 2289–2294. http://doi.org/10.1080/17470218.2013.858170

Franklin, M. S., Smallwood, J., & Schooler, J. W. (2011). Catching the mind in flight: Using behavioral indices to detect mindless reading in real time. *Psychonomic Bulletin & Review, 18*(5), 992–997. http://doi.org/10.3758/s13423-011-0109-6

Fresco, D. M., Moore, M. T., van Dulmen, M. H. M., Segal, Z. V, Ma, S. H., Teasdale, J. D., & Williams, J. M. G. (2007). Initial psychometric properties of the experiences questionnaire: Validation of a self-report measure of decentering. *Behavior Therapy, 38*(3), 234–246.

Fuchs, C., Lee, J. K., Roemer, L., & Orsillo, S. M. (2013). Using mindfulness- and acceptance-based treatments with clients from nondominant cultural and/or marginalized backgrounds: Clinical considerations, meta-analysis findings, and introduction to the special series. *Cognitive and Behavioral Practice, 20*(1), 1–12.

Gale, C., Gilbert, P., Read, N., & Goss, K. (2014). An evaluation of the impact of introducing compassion focused therapy to a standard treatment programme for people with eating disorders. *Clinical Psychology and Psychotherapy, 21*(1), 1–12. http://doi.org/10.1002/cpp.1806

Garland, E. L., Froeliger, B., & Howard, M. O. (2014). Effects of Mindfulness-Oriented Recovery Enhancement on reward responsiveness and opioid cue-reactivity. *Psychopharmacology, 231*(16), 3229–3238. http://doi.org/10.1007/s00213-014-3504-7

Garland, E. L., Roberts-Lewis, A., Tronnier, C. D., Graves, R., & Kelley, K. (2015). Mindfulness-Oriented Recovery Enhancement versus CBT for co-occurring substance dependence, traumatic stress, and psychiatric disorders: Proximal outcomes from a pragmatic randomized trial. *Behaviour Research and Therapy, 77*, 7–16.

Garrison, K. A., Scheinost, D., Worhunsky, P. D., Elwafi, H. M., Thornhill, T. A., Thompson, E., … Brewer, J. A. (2013). Real-time fMRI links subjective experience with brain activity during focused attention. *NeuroImage, 81*, 110–118. http://doi.org/10.1016/j.neuroimage.2013.05.030

Germer, C. K., Siegel, R. D., & Fulton, P. R. (2013). *Mindfulness and psychotherapy*. New York, NY: Guilford Press.

Gethin, R. (2011). On some definitions of mindfulness. *Contemporary Buddhism, 12*(1), 263–279. http://doi.org/10.1080/14639947.2011.564843

Gilbert, P. (2009). Developing a compassion-focused approach in cognitive behavioural therapy. In G. Simos (Ed.), *Cognitive behaviour therapy: A guide for the practising clinician* (Vol 2 , pp 205–220). New York, NY: Routledge.

Gilbert, P. (2010). An introduction to compassion focused therapy in cognitive behavior therapy. *International Journal of Cognitive Therapy, 3*(2), 97–112. http://doi.org/10.1521/ijct.2010.3.2.97

Gilbert, P., & Procter, S. (2006). Compassionate mind training for people with high shame and self-criticism: Overview and pilot study of a group therapy approach. *Clinical Psychology and Psychotherapy, 13*, 353–379. http://doi.org/10.1002/cpp.507

Godfrey, K. M., Gallo, L. C., & Afari, N. (2015). Mindfulness-based interventions for binge eating: A systematic review and meta-analysis. *Journal of Behavioral Medicine, 38*(2), 348–362. http://doi.org/10.1007/s10865-014-9610-5

Goldberg, S. B., Wielgosz, J., Dahl, C., Schuyler, B., MacCoon, D. S., Rosenkranz, M., ... Davidson, R. J. (2015). Does the Five Facet Mindfulness Questionnaire measure what we think it does? Construct validity evidence from an active controlled randomized clinical trial. *Psychological Assessment, 28*(8), 1009–1014.

Goldstein, J. (1980). *The experience of insight: A natural unfolding.* Boston, MA: Shambhala Publications.

Greeson, J., & Eisenlohr-Moul, T. (2014). Mindfulness-based stress reduction for chronic pain. In R. Baer (Ed.), *Mindfulness-based treatment approaches: Clinician's guide to evidence based and applications* (2nd ed., pp. 269–292). Burlington, MA: Academic Press. http://doi.org/10.1016/B978-0-12-416031-6.00012-8

Gregg, J. A., Callaghan, G. M., Hayes, S. C., & Glenn-Lawson, J. L. (2007). Improving diabetes self-management through acceptance, mindfulness, and values: A randomized controlled trial. *Journal of Consulting and Clinical Psychology, 75*(2), 336–343. http://doi.org/10.1037/0022-006X.75.2.336

Gross, C. R., Kreitzer, M. J., Reilly-Spong, M., Wall, M., Winbush, N. Y., Patterson, R., ... Cramer-Bornemann, M. (2011). Mindfulness-based stress reduction versus pharmacotherapy for chronic primary insomnia: A randomized controlled clinical trial. *Explore: The Journal of Science and Healing, 7*(2), 76–87.

Gross, J. J. (2015). Emotion regulation: Current status and future prospects. *Psychological Inquiry, 26*(1), 1–26. http://doi.org/10.1080/1047840X.2014.940781

Grossman, P. (2011). Defining mindfulness by how poorly I think I pay attention during everyday awareness and other intractable problems for psychology's (re)invention of mindfulness: Comment on Brown et al. (2011). *Psychological Assessment, 23*(4), 1034–1046.

Grossman, P. (2015). Mindfulness: Awareness informed by an embodied ethic. *Mindfulness, 6*(1), 17–22. http://doi.org/10.1007/s12671-014-0372-5

Grossman, P., Niemann, L., Schmidt, S., & Walach, H. (2004). Mindfulness-based stress reduction and health benefits. A meta-analysis. *Journal of Psychosomatic Research, 57*(1), 35–43. http://doi.org/10.1016/S0022-3999(03)00573-7

Grossman, P., Tiefenthaler-Gilmer, U., Raysz, A., & Kesper, U. (2007). Mindfulness training as an intervention for fibromyalgia: Evidence of postintervention and 3-year follow-up benefits in well-being. *Psychotherapy and Psychosomatics, 76*(4), 226–233. http://doi.org/10.1159/000101501

Gu, J., Strauss, C., Bond, R., & Cavanagh, K. (2015). How do mindfulness-based cognitive therapy and mindfulness-based stress reduction improve mental health and wellbeing? A systematic review and meta-analysis of mediation studies. *Clinical Psychology Review, 37*, 1–12.

Gumley, A., Braehler, C., Laithwaite, H., MacBeth, A., & Gilbert, P. (2010). A compassion focused model of recovery after psychosis. *International Journal of Cognitive Therapy, 3*(2), 186–201. http://doi.org/10.1521/ijct.2010.3.2.186

Haigh, E. A. P., Moore, M. T., Kashdan, T. B., & Fresco, D. M. (2011). Examination of the factor structure and concurrent validity of the Langer Mindfulness/Mindlessness Scale. *Assessment, 18*(1), 11–26. http://doi.org/10.1177/1073191110386342

Halifax, J. (2011). The precious necessity of compassion. *Journal of Pain and Symptom Management, 41*(1), 146–153. http://doi.org/10.1016/j.jpainsymman.2010.08.010

Hayes, S. C., Levin, M. E., Plumb-Vilardaga, J., Villatte, J. L., & Pistorello, J. (2013). Acceptance and commitment therapy and contextual behavioral science: Examining the progress of a distinctive model of behavioral and cognitive therapy. *Behavior Therapy, 44*(2), 180–198.

Hayes, S. C., Luoma, J. B., Bond, F. W., Masuda, A., & Lillis, J. (2006). Acceptance and commitment therapy: Model, processes and outcomes. *Behaviour Research and Therapy, 44*(1), 1–25. http://doi.org/10.1016/j.brat.2005.06.006

Hayes, S. C., Pistorello, J., & Levin, M. E. (2012). Acceptance and commitment therapy as a unified model of behavior change. *The Counseling Psychologist, 40*(7), 976–1002. http://doi.org/10.1177/0011000012460836

Hayes, S. C., Strosahl, K. D., & Wilson, K. G. (1999). *Acceptance and commitment therapy: An experiential approach to behavior change*. New York, NY: Guilford Press.

Hayes, S. C., Strosahl, K., & Wilson, K. G. (2013). *Acceptance and commitment therapy: The practice and process of mindful change* (2nd ed.). New York, NY: Guilford Press.

Hayes, S. C., & Wilson, K. G. (2003). Mindfulness: Method and process. *Clinical Psychology: Science and Practice, 10*(2), 161–165. http://doi.org/10.1093/clipsy.bpg018

Hinton, D. E., Pich, V., Hofmann, S. G., & Otto, M. W. (2013). Acceptance and mindfulness techniques as applied to refugee and ethnic minority populations with PTSD: Examples from "Culturally Adapted CBT." *Cognitive and Behavioral Practice, 20*(1), 33–46. http://doi.org/10.1016/j.cbpra.2011.09.001

Hofmann, S. G., Grossman, P., & Hinton, D. E. (2011). Loving-kindness and compassion meditation: Potential for psychological interventions. *Clinical Psychology Review, 31*(7), 1126–1132. http://doi.org/10.1016/j.cpr.2011.07.003

Hofmann, S. G., Sawyer, A. T., Witt, A. A., & Oh, D. (2010). The effect of mindfulness-based therapy on anxiety and depression: A meta-analytic review. *Journal of Consulting and Clinical Psychology, 78*(2), 169–183. http://doi.org/10.1037/a0018555

Hölzel, B. K., Carmody, J., Evans, K. C., Hoge, E. A., Dusek, J. A., Morgan, L., … Lazar, S. W. (2010). Stress reduction correlates with structural changes in the amygdala. *Social Cognitive and Affective Neuroscience, 5*(1), 11–7. http://doi.org/10.1093/scan/nsp034

Hölzel, B. K., Carmody, J., Vangel, M., Congleton, C., Yerramsetti, S. M., Gard, T., & Lazar, S. W. (2011). Mindfulness practice leads to increases in regional brain gray matter density. *Psychiatry Research, 191*(1), 36–43. http://doi.org/10.1016/j.pscychresns.2010.08.006

Hölzel, B. K., Lazar, S. W., Gard, T., Schuman-Olivier, Z., Vago, D. R., & Ott, U. (2011). How does mindfulness meditation work? Proposing mechanisms of action from a conceptual and neural perspective. *Perspectives on Psychological Science, 6*, 537–559. http://doi.org/10.1177/1745691611419671

Irving, J. A., Park-Saltzman, J., Fitzpatrick, M., Dobkin, P. L., Chen, A., & Hutchinson, T. (2012). Experiences of health care professionals enrolled in mindfulness-based medical practice: A grounded theory model. *Mindfulness, 5*(1), 60–71. http://doi.org/10.1007/s12671-012-0147-9

Ives-Deliperi, V. L., Howells, F., Stein, D. J., Meintjes, E. M., & Horn, N. (2013). The effects of mindfulness-based cognitive therapy in patients with bipolar disorder: A controlled functional MRI investigation. *Journal of Affective Disorders, 150*(3), 1152–1157. http://doi.org/10.1016/j.jad.2013.05.074

Jha, A. P., Krompinger, J., & Baime, M. J. (2007). Mindfulness training modifies subsystems of attention. *Cognitive, Affective & Behavioral Neuroscience, 7*(2), 109–119. http://doi.org/10.3758/CABN.7.2.109

Judge, L., Cleghorn, A., McEwan, K., & Gilbert, P. (2012). An exploration of group-based compassion focused therapy for a heterogeneous range of clients presenting to a community mental health team. *International Journal of Cognitive Therapy, 5*(4), 420–429. http://doi.org/10.1521/ijct.2012.5.4.420

Kabat-Zinn, J. (2002). Commentary on Majumdar et al.: Mindfulness meditation for health. *The Journal of Alternative & Complementary Medicine, 8*(6), 731–735. http://doi.org/10.1089/10755530260511739

Kabat-Zinn, J. (2003). Mindfulness-based interventions in context: Past, present, and future. *Clinical Psychology: Science and Practice, 10*(2), 144–156. http://doi.org/10.1093/clipsy.bpg016

Kabat-Zinn, J., Lipworth, L., & Burney, R. (1985). The clinical use of mindfulness meditation for the self-regulation of chronic pain. *Journal of Behavioral Medicine, 8*(2), 163–190. http://doi.org/10.1007/BF00845519

Kabat-Zinn, J., Wheeler, E., Light, T., Skillings, A., Scharf, M. J., Cropley, T. G., … Bernhard, J. D. (1998). Influence of a mindfulness meditation-based stress reduction intervention on rates of skin clearing in patients with moderate to severe psoriasis undergoing photo therapy (UVB) and photochemotherapy (PUVA). *Psychosomatic Medicine, 60*(5), 625–632.

Kaliman, P., Alvarez-López, M. J., Cosín-Tomás, M., Rosenkranz, M. A., Lutz, A., & Davidson, R. J. (2014). Rapid changes in histone deacetylases and inflammatory gene expression in expert meditators. *Psychoneuroendocrinology, 40*, 96–107. http://doi.org/10.1016/j.psyneuen.2013.11.004

Karekla, M., & Panayiotou, G. (2011). Coping and experiential avoidance: Unique or overlapping constructs? *Journal of Behavior Therapy and Experimental Psychiatry, 42*(2), 163–170.

Kashdan, T. B., & Rottenberg, J. (2010). Psychological flexibility as a fundamental aspect of health. *Clinical Psychology Review, 30*(7), 865–878. http://doi.org/10.1016/j.cpr.2010.03.001

Kato, T. (2012). Development of the Coping Flexibility Scale: Evidence for the coping flexibility hypothesis. *Journal of Counseling Psychology, 59*(2), 262–273. http://doi.org/10.1037/a0027770

Keng, S.-L., Smoski, M. J., & Robins, C. J. (2011). Effects of mindfulness on psychological health: A review of empirical studies. *Clinical Psychology Review, 31*(6), 1041–1056. http://doi.org/10.1016/j.cpr.2011.04.006

Khoury, B., Lecomte, T., Fortin, G., Masse, M., Therien, P., Bouchard, V., ... Hofmann, S. G. (2013). Mindfulness-based therapy: A comprehensive meta-analysis. *Clinical Psychology Review, 33*(6), 763–771. http://doi.org/10.1016/j.cpr.2013.05.005

Khoury, B., Lecomte, T., Gaudiano, B. A., & Paquin, K. (2013). Mindfulness interventions for psychosis: A meta-analysis. *Schizophrenia Research, 150*(1), 176–184. http://doi.org/10.1016/j.schres.2013.07.055

Kiken, L. G., Garland, E. L., Bluth, K., Palsson, O. S., & Gaylord, S. A. (2015). From a state to a trait: Trajectories of state mindfulness in meditation during intervention predict changes in trait mindfulness. *Personality and Individual Differences, 81*, 41–46.

Kiken, L. G., & Shook, N. J. (2014). Does mindfulness attenuate thoughts emphasizing negativity, but not positivity? *Journal of Research in Personality, 53*, 22–30.

Killingsworth, M. A., & Gilbert, D. T. (2010). A wandering mind is an unhappy mind. *Science, 330*(6006), 932. http://doi.org/10.1126/science.1192439

Kliem, S., Kröger, C., & Kosfelder, J. (2010). Dialectical behavior therapy for borderline personality disorder: A meta-analysis using mixed-effects modeling. *Journal of Consulting and Clinical Psychology, 78*(6), 936–951. http://doi.org/10.1037/a0021015

Kohls, N., Sauer, S., & Walach, H. (2009). Facets of mindfulness – Results of an online study investigating the Freiburg Mindfulness Inventory. *Personality and Individual Differences, 46*(2), 224–230. http://doi.org/10.1016/j.paid.2008.10.009

Krasner, M. S., Epstein, R. M., Beckman, H., Suchman, A. L., Chapman, B., Mooney, C. J., & Quill, T. E. (2009). Association of an educational program in mindful communication with burnout, empathy, and attitudes among primary care physicians. *JAMA, 302*(12), 1284–1293.

Kristeller, J. L., & Wolever, R. Q. (2011). Mindfulness-based eating awareness training for treating binge eating disorder: the conceptual foundation. *Eating Disorders, 19*(1), 49–61. http://doi.org/10.1080/10640266.2011.533605

Kristeller, J. L., Wolever, R. Q., & Sheets, V. (2013). Mindfulness-based eating awareness training (MB-EAT) for binge eating: A randomized clinical trial. *Mindfulness, 5*(3), 282–297. http://doi.org/10.1007/s12671-012-0179-1

Langer, E. F. (1989). *Mindfulness*. Cambridge, MA: De Capo Press.

Lau, M. A., Bishop, S. R., Segal, Z. V., Buis, T., Anderson, N. D., Carlson, L., ... Devins, G. (2006). The Toronto Mindfulness Scale: Development and validation. *Journal of Clinical Psychology, 62*(12), 1445–1467. http://doi.org/10.1002/jclp.20326

Lazar, S. W., Kerr, C. E., Wasserman, R. H., Gray, J. R., Greve, D. N., Treadway, M. T., ... Fischl, B. (2005). Meditation experience is associated with increased cortical thickness. *Neuroreport, 16*(17), 1893–1897. http://doi.org/10.1097/01.wnr.0000186598.66243.19

Leaviss, J., & Uttley, L. (2015). Psychotherapeutic benefits of compassion-focused therapy: An early systematic review. *Psychological Medicine, 45*(5), 927–945. http://doi.org/10.1017/S0033291714002141

Lee, J., Semple, R. J., Rosa, D., & Miller, L. (2008). Mindfulness-based cognitive therapy for children: Results of a pilot study. *Journal of Cognitive Psychotherapy, 22*(1), 15–28. http://doi.org/10.1891/0889.8391.22.1.15

Levinson, D. B., Stoll, E. L., Kindy, S. D., Merry, H. L., & Davidson, R. J. (2014). A mind you can count on: Validating breath counting as a behavioral measure of mindfulness. *Frontiers in Psychology, 5*, 1202. http://doi.org/10.3389/fpsyg.2014.01202

Li, M. J., Black, D. S., & Garland, E. L. (2016). The Applied Mindfulness Process Scale (AMPS): A process measure for evaluating mindfulness-based interventions. *Personality and Individual Differences, 93*, 6–15. http://doi.org/10.1016/j.paid.2015.10.027

Lindahl, J. R. (2015). Why right mindfulness might not be right for mindfulness. *Mindfulness, 6*(1), 57–62. http://doi.org/10.1007/s12671-014-0380-5

Linehan, M. M. (1993a). *Cognitive-behavioral treatment for borderline personality disorder*. New York, NY: Guilford Press.

Linehan, M. M. (1993b). *Skills training manual for treating borderline personality disorder*. New York, NY: Guilford Press.

Lloyd, D. M., Mason, L., Brown, R. J., & Poliakoff, E. (2008). Development of a paradigm for measuring somatic disturbance in clinical populations with medically unexplained symptoms. *Journal of Psychosomatic Research, 64*(1), 21–24. http://doi.org/10.1016/j.jpsychores.2007.06.004

Lucre, K. M., & Corten, N. (2013). An exploration of group compassion-focused therapy for personality disorder. *Psychology and Psychotherapy: Theory, Research and Practice, 86*(4), 387–400. http://doi.org/10.1111/j.2044-8341.2012.02068.x

Lustyk, M. K., Chawla, N., Nolan, R. S., & Marlatt, G. A. (2009). Mindfulness mediation research: Issues of participant screening, safety procedures and researcher training. *Advances in Mind Body Medicine, 24*(1), 20–30.

Lutz, A., Jha, A. P., Dunne, J. D., & Saron, C. D. (2015). Investigating the phenomenological matrix of mindfulness-related practices from a neurocognitive perspective. *American Psychologist, 70*(7), 632–358. http://doi.org/10.1037/a0039585

Lutz, A., Slagter, H. A., Rawlings, N. B., Francis, A. D., Greischar, L. L., & Davidson, R. J. (2009). Mental training enhances attentional stability: Neural and behavioral evidence. *Journal of Neuroscience, 29*(42), 13418–13427. http://doi.org/10.1523/JNEUROSCI.1614-09.2009

Lyvers, M., Makin, C., Toms, E., Thorberg, F. A., & Samios, C. (2013). Trait mindfulness in relation to emotional self-regulation and executive function. *Mindfulness, 5*(6), 619–625. http://doi.org/10.1007/s12671-013-0213-y

Malinowski, P., & Lim, H. J. (2015). Mindfulness at work: Positive affect, hope, and optimism mediate the relationship between dispositional mindfulness, work engagement, and well-being. *Mindfulness, 6*(6), 1–13. http://doi.org/10.1007/s12671-015-0388-5

Marlatt, G. A., & Gordon, J. R. (1985). *Relapse prevention: Maintenance strategies in addictive behaviour change*. New York, NY: Guilford Press.

McCown, D., Reibel, D., & Micozzi, M. S. (2011). *Teaching mindfulness: A practical guide for clinicians and educators*. New York, NY: Springer.

Mehling, W. E., Price, C., Daubenmier, J. J., Acree, M., Bartmess, E., & Stewart, A. (2012). The Multidimensional Assessment of Interoceptive Awareness (MAIA). *PLoS ONE, 7*(11), e48230. http://doi.org/10.1371/journal.pone.0048230

Miller, W. R., & Rollnick, S. (2013). *Motivational interviewing: Helping people change* (3rd ed.). New York; NY: Guilford Press.

Mirams, L., Poliakoff, E., Brown, R. J., & Lloyd, D. M. (2013). Brief body-scan meditation practice improves somatosensory perceptual decision making. *Consciousness and Cognition, 22*(1), 348–359. http://doi.org/10.1016/j.concog.2012.07.009

Mitchell, J. T., Zylowska, L., & Kollins, S. H. (2015). Mindfulness meditation training for attention-deficit/hyperactivity disorder in adulthood: Current empirical support, treatment overview, and future directions. *Cognitive and Behavioral Practice, 22*(2), 172–191.

Monteiro, L. M., Musten, R. F., & Compson, J. (2015). Traditional and contemporary mindfulness: Finding the middle path in the tangle of concerns. *Mindfulness, 6*(1), 1–13. http://doi.org/10.1007/s12671-014-0301-7

Mrazek, M. D., Smallwood, J., & Schooler, J. W. (2012). Mindfulness and mind-wandering: Finding convergence through opposing constructs. *Emotion, 12*(3), 442–8. http://doi.org/10.1037/a0026678

Neff, K. D. (2003). Development and validation of a scale to measure self-compassion. *Self and Identity, 2*, 223–250. http://doi.org/10.1080/15298860309027

Nesvold, A., Fagerland, M. W., Davanger, S., Ellingsen, Ø., Solberg, E. E., Holen, A., … Atar, D. (2012). Increased heart rate variability during nondirective meditation. *European Journal of Preventive Cardiology, 19*(4), 773–780. http://doi.org/10.1177/1741826711414625

Nolen-Hoeksema, S., Wisco, B. E., & Lyubomirsky, S. (2008). Rethinking rumination. *Perspectives on Psychological Science, 3*(5), 400–424. http://doi.org/10.1111/j.1745-6924.2008.00088.x

Normann, N., Emmerik, A. A. P., & Morina, N. (2014). The efficacy of metacognitive therapy for anxiety and depression: A meta-analytic review. *Depression and Anxiety, 31*(5), 402–411. http://doi.org/10.1002/da.22273

Olendzki, A. (2011). The construction of mindfulness. *Contemporary Buddhism, 12*(1), 55–70. http://doi.org/10.1080/14639947.2011.564817

Ong, J. C., Manber, R., Segal, Z., Xia, Y., Shapiro, S., & Wyatt, J. K. (2014). A randomized controlled trial of mindfulness meditation for chronic insomnia. *Sleep, 37*, 1553–1563. http://doi.org/10.5665/sleep.4010

Ong, J. C., & Sholtes, D. (2010). A mindfulness-based approach to the treatment of insomnia. *Journal of Clinical Psychology, 66*(11), 1175–1184. http://doi.org/10.1002/jclp.20736

Ong, J. C., Ulmer, C. S., & Manber, R. (2012). Improving sleep with mindfulness and acceptance: A metacognitive model of insomnia. *Behaviour Research and Therapy, 50*(11), 651–660. http://doi.org/10.1016/j.brat.2012.08.001

Öst, L. G. (2008). Efficacy of the third wave of behavioral therapies: A systematic review and meta-analysis. *Behaviour Research and Therapy, 46*(3), 296–321.

Ostafin, B. D., & Kassman, K. T. (2012). Stepping out of history: Mindfulness improves insight problem solving. *Consciousness and Cognition, 21*(2), 1031–1036. http://doi.org/10.1016/j.concog.2012.02.014

Otto, M. W. (2000). Stories and metaphors in cognitive-behavior therapy. *Cognitive and Behavioral Practice, 7*(2), 166–172. http://doi.org/10.1016/S1077-7229(00)80027-9

Panos, P. T., Jackson, J. W., Hasan, O., & Panos, A. (2013). Meta-analysis and systematic review assessing the efficacy of dialectical behavior therapy (DBT). *Research on Social Work Practice, 24*(2), 213–223. http://doi.org/10.1177/1049731513503047

Park, T., Reilly-Spong, M., & Gross, C. R. (2013). Mindfulness: A systematic review of instruments to measure an emergent patient-reported outcome (PRO). *Quality of Life Research, 22*(10), 2639–2659. http://doi.org/10.1007/s11136-013-0395-8

Piet, J., & Hougaard, E. (2011). The effect of mindfulness-based cognitive therapy for prevention of relapse in recurrent major depressive disorder: A systematic review and meta-analysis. *Clinical Psychology Review, 31*(6), 1032–1040. http://doi.org/10.1016/j.cpr.2011.05.002

Piet, J., Würtzen, H., & Zachariae, R. (2012). The effect of mindfulness-based therapy on symptoms of anxiety and depression in adult cancer patients and survivors: A systematic review and meta-analysis. *Journal of Consulting and Clinical Psychology, 80*(6), 1007–1020.

Pollak, S. M., Pedulla, T., & Siegel, R. D. (2014). *Sitting together: Essential skills for mindfulness-based psychotherapy*. New York, NY: Guilford Press.

Pomykala, K. L., Silverman, D. H., Geist, C. L., Voege, P., Siddarth, P., Nazarian, N., … Lavretsky, H. (2012). A pilot study of the effects of meditation on regional brain metabolism in distressed dementia caregivers. *Aging Health, 8*(5), 509–516. http://doi.org/10.2217/ahe.12.46

Pradhan, E. K., Baumgarten, M., Langenberg, P., Handwerger, B., Gilpin, A. K., Magyari, T., … Berman, B. M. (2007). Effect of mindfulness-based stress reduction in rheumatoid arthritis patients. *Arthritis Care & Research, 57*(7), 1134–1142. http://doi.org/10.1002/art.23010

Pull, C. B. (2009). Current empirical status of acceptance and commitment therapy. *Current Opinion in Psychiatry, 22*(1), 55–60. http://doi.org/10.1097/YCO.0b013e32831a6e9d

Purser, R. E., & Milillo, J. (2015). Mindfulness revisited: A Buddhist-based conceptualization. *Journal of Management Inquiry, 24*(1), 3–24. http://doi.org/10.1177/1056492614532315

Rau, H. K., & Williams, P. G. (2016). Dispositional mindfulness: A critical review of construct validation research. *Personality and Individual Differences, 93*, 32–43. http://doi.org/10.1016/j.paid.2015.09.035

Rinpoche, K. T. (2011). *The Ninth Karmapa's ocean of definitive meaning.* Boston, MA: Shambhala Publications.

Robertson, I. H., Manly, T., Andrade, J., Baddeley, B. T., & Yiend, J. (1997). "Oops!": Performance correlates of everyday attentional failures in traumatic brain injured and normal subjects. *Neuropsychologia, 35*(6), 747–758. http://doi.org/10.1016/S0028-3932(97)00015-8

Roemer, L., Williston, S. K., & Rollins, L. G. (2015). Mindfulness and emotion regulation. *Current Opinion in Psychology, 3*, 52–57. http://doi.org/10.1016/j.copsyc.2015.02.006

Rogers, B., Christopher, M., & Bilgen-Sunbay, Z. (2013). Mindfulness, self-care, and participatory medicine: A community's clinical evidence. *Journal of Participatory Medicine, 5*, e9.

Rosch, E. (2003). The basis of Compassion: Western science in dialog with the Dalai Lama. *PsycCRITIQUES, 48*(3), 330–332. http://doi.org/10.1037/000807

Rosenkranz, M. A., Davidson, R. J., Maccoon, D. G., Sheridan, J. F., Kalin, N. H., & Lutz, A. (2012). A comparison of mindfulness-based stress reduction and an active control in modulation of neurogenic inflammation. *Brain, Behavior, and Immunity, 27*(1), 174–184.

Rosenzweig, S., Reibel, D. K., Greeson, J. M., Edman, J. S., Jasser, S. A., McMearty, K. D., & Goldstein, B. J. (2007). Mindfulness-based stress reduction is associated with improved glycemic control in type 2 diabetes mellitus: A pilot study. *Alternative Therapies in Health and Medicine, 13*(5), 36–38.

Ruiz Jiménez, F. J. (2012). Acceptance and commitment therapy versus traditional cognitive behavioral therapy: A systematic review and meta-analysis of current empirical evidence. *International Journal of Psychology and Psychological Therapy, 12*(3), 333–358.

Salzberg, S. (2011). Mindfulness and loving-kindness. *Contemporary Buddhism, 12*(1), 177–182. http://doi.org/10.1080/14639947.2011.564837

Sayadaw, M. (1994). *The progress of insight: Treatise on Buddhist Satipathana meditation.* Kandy, Sri Lanka: Buddhist Publication Society.

Sayette, M. A., Schooler, J. W., & Reichle, E. D. (2010). Out for a smoke: The impact of cigarette craving on zoning out during reading. *Psychological Science, 21*(1), 26–30. http://doi.org/10.1177/0956797609354059

Schutte, N. S., & Malouff, J. M. (2014). A meta-analytic review of the effects of mindfulness meditation on telomerase activity. *Psychoneuroendocrinology, 42*, 45–48. http://doi.org/10.1016/j.psyneuen.2013.12.017

Segal, Z. V, Bieling, P., Young, T., MacQueen, G., Cooke, R., Martin, L., … Levitan, R. D. (2010). Antidepressant monotherapy vs sequential pharmacotherapy and mindfulness-based cognitive therapy, or placebo, for relapse prophylaxis in recurrent depression. *Archives of General Psychiatry, 67*(12), 1256–1264.

Segal, Z. V., Williams, J. M., & Teasdale, J. D. (2002). *Mindfulness-based cognitive therapy for depression: A new approach to preventing relapse.* New York, NY: Guilford Press.

Segal, Z. V., Williams, J. M., Teasdale, J. D., & Gemar, M. (1996). A cognitive science perspective on kindling and episode sensitization in recurrent affective disorder. *Psychological Medicine, 26*(2), 371–380. http://doi.org/10.1017/S0033291700034760

Shalev, L., Ben-Simon, A., Mevorach, C., Cohen, Y., & Tsal, Y. (2011). Conjunctive Continuous Performance Task (CCPT) – A pure measure of sustained attention. *Neuropsychologia, 49*(9), 2584–2591. http://doi.org/10.1016/j.neuropsychologia.2011.05.006

Shapiro, S. L., Carlson, L. E., Astin, J. A., & Freedman, B. (2006). Mechanisms of mindfulness. *Journal of Clinical Psychology, 62*(3), 373–386. http://doi.org/10.1002/jclp.20237

Shapiro, S., Thakur, S., & de Sousa, S. (2014). Mindfulness for health care professionals and therapists in training. In R. A. Baer (Ed.), *Mindfulness-based treatment approaches: Clinician's guide to evidence base and applications* (pp. 319–345). San Diego, CA: Academic Press. http://doi.org/10.1016/B978-0-12-416031-6.00014-1

Shennan, C., Payne, S., & Fenlon, D. (2011). What is the evidence for the use of mindfulness-based interventions in cancer care? A review. *Psycho-Oncology, 20*(7), 681–697. http://doi.org/10.1002/pon.1819

Shonin, E., Van Gordon, W., & Griffiths, M. D. (2013). Mindfulness-based interventions: Towards mindful clinical integration. *Frontiers in Psychology, 4*, 194. http://doi.org/10.3389/fpsyg.2013.00194

Siegling, A. B., & Petrides, K. V. (2014). Measures of trait mindfulness: Convergent validity, shared dimensionality, and linkages to the five-factor model. *Frontiers in Psychology, 5*, 1164. http://doi.org/10.3389/fpsyg.2014.01164

Slagter, H. A., Davidson, R. J., & Lutz, A. (2011). Mental training as a tool in the neuroscientific study of brain and cognitive plasticity. *Frontiers in Human Neuroscience, 5*, 17. http://doi.org/10.3389/fnhum.2011.00017

Smallwood, J., Mrazek, M. D., & Schooler, J. W. (2011). Medicine for the wandering mind: Mind wandering in medical practice. *Medical Education, 45*(11), 1072–1080. http://doi.org/10.1111/j.1365-2923.2011.04074.x

Smith, P. L., & Ratcliff, R. (2009). An integrated theory of attention and decision making in visual signal detection. *Psychological Review, 116*(2), 283–317. http://doi.org/10.1037/a0015156

Sobczak, L. T. R., & West, L. M. (2011). Clinical considerations in using mindfulness-and acceptance-based approaches with diverse populations: Addressing challenges in service delivery in diverse community settings. *Cognitive and Behavioral Practice, 20*(1), 13–22.

Soler, J., Valdepérez, A., Feliu-Soler, A., Pascual, J. C., Portella, M. J., Martin-Blanco, A., ... Perez, V. (2012). Effects of the dialectical behavioral therapy mindfulness module on attention in patients with borderline personality disorder. *Behaviour Research and Therapy, 50*(2), 150–157.

Sperduti, M., Martinelli, P., & Piolino, P. (2012). A neurocognitive model of meditation based on activation likelihood estimation (ALE) meta-analysis. *Consciousness and Cognition, 21*(1), 269–276. http://doi.org/10.1016/j.concog.2011.09.019

Tanay, G., & Bernstein, A. (2013). State Mindfulness Scale (SMS): Development and initial validation. *Psychological Assessment, 25*(4), 1286–1299. http://doi.org/10.1037/a0034044

Teasdale, J. D., Moore, R. G., Hayhurst, H., Pope, M., Williams, S., & Segal, Z. V. (2002). Metacognitive awareness and prevention of relapse in depression: Empirical evidence. *Journal of Consulting and Clinical Psychology, 70*(2), 275–287. http://doi.org/10.1037/0022-006X.70.2.275

Ṭhānissaro, B. (2012). *Right mindfulness: Memory and ardency on the Buddhist path.* Valley Center, CA: Metta Forest Monastery.

Thayer, J. F., & Sternberg, E. (2006). Beyond heart rate variability: Vagal regulation of allostatic systems. *Annals of the New York Academy of Sciences, 1088*, 361–372. http://doi.org/10.1196/annals.1366.014

Tirch, D., & Gilbert, P. (2015). Compassion-focused therapy: An introduction to experiential interventions for cultivating compassion. In N. C. Thoma & D. McKay (Eds.), *Working with emotion in cognitive-behavioral therapy: Techniques for clinical practice.* (pp. 59–79). New York, NY: Guilford Press.

Tomasino, B., Chiesa, A., & Fabbro, F. (2014). Disentangling the neural mechanisms involved in Hinduism- and Buddhism-related meditations. *Brain and Cognition, 90*, 32–40. http://doi.org/10.1016/j.bandc.2014.03.013

Tovote, K. A., Fleer, J., Snippe, E., Peeters, A. C. T. M., Emmelkamp, P. M. G., Sanderman, R., ... Schroevers, M. J. (2014). Individual mindfulness-based cognitive therapy and cognitive behavior therapy for treating depressive symptoms in patients with diabetes: Results of a randomized controlled trial. *Diabetes Care, 37*(9), 2427–2434.

Tran, U. S., Glück, T. M., & Nader, I. W. (2013). Investigating the Five Facet Mindfulness Questionnaire (FFMQ): Construction of a short form and evidence of a two-factor higher order structure of mindfulness. *Journal of Clinical Psychology, 69*(9), 951–965. http://doi.org/10.1002/jclp.21996

Vago, D. R., & Silbersweig, D. A. (2012). Self-awareness, self-regulation, and self-transcendence (S-ART): A framework for understanding the neurobiological mechanisms of mindfulness. *Frontiers in Human Neuroscience, 6*, 296. http://doi.org/10.3389/fnhum.2012.00296

van der Valk, R., van de Waerdt, S., Meijer, C. J., van den Hout, I., & de Haan, L. (2013). Feasibility of mindfulness-based therapy in patients recovering from a first psychotic episode: A pilot study. *Early Intervention in Psychiatry, 7*(1), 64–70. http://doi.org/10.1111/j.1751-7893.2012.00356.x

Van Gordon, W., Shonin, E., Griffiths, M. D., & Singh, N. N. (2014). There is only one mindfulness: Why science and Buddhism need to work together. *Mindfulness, 6*(1), 49–56. http://doi.org/10.1007/s12671-014-0379-y

Veehof, M. M., Oskam, M.-J., Schreurs, K. M. G., & Bohlmeijer, E. T. (2011). Acceptance-based interventions for the treatment of chronic pain: A systematic review and meta-analysis. *Pain, 152*(3), 533–542. http://doi.org/10.1016/j.pain.2010.11.002

Waelde, L. C., Thompson, J. M., Robinson, A., & Iwanicki, S. (2016). Trauma therapists' clinical applications, training, and personal practice of mindfulness and meditation. *Mindfulness, 7*, 622–629. http://doi.org/10.1007/s12671-016-0497-9

Wagner, A. W., & Linehan, M. M. (2007). Applications of dialectical behavior therapy to posttraumatic stress disorder and related problems. In V. M. Follette & J. I. Ruzek (Eds.), *Cognitive-behavioral therapies for trauma* (pp. 117–145). New York, NY: Guilford Press.

Walach, H., Buchheld, N., Buttenmuller, V., Kleinknecht, N., & Schmidt, S. (2006). Measuring mindfulness – The Freiburg Mindfulness Inventory (FMI). *Personality and Individual Differences, 40*, 1543–1555. http://doi.org/10.1016/j.paid.2005.11.025

Wallace, R. K. (1970). Physiological effects of transcendental meditation. *Science, 167*(3926), 1751–1754.

Wanden-Berghe, R. G., Sanz-Valero, J., & Wanden-Berghe, C. (2010). The application of mindfulness to eating disorders treatment: A systematic review. *Eating Disorders, 19*(1), 34–48. http://doi.org/10.1080/10640266.2011.533604

Wells, A. (2000). *Emotional disorders and metacognition: Innovative cognitive therapy.* New York, NY: Wiley.

Wells, A. (2005). Detached mindfulness in cognitive therapy: A metacognitive analysis and ten techniques. *Journal of Rational-Emotive and Cognitive-Behavior Therapy, 23*(4), 337–355. http://doi.org/10.1007/s10942-005-0018-6

Wells, A., & Matthews, G. (1996). Modelling cognition in emotional disorder: The S-REF model. *Behaviour Research and Therapy, 34*(11), 881–888. http://doi.org/10.1016/S0005-7967(96)00050-2

Wells, A., Walton, D., Lovell, K., & Proctor, D. (2014). Metacognitive therapy versus prolonged exposure in adults with chronic post-traumatic stress disorder: A parallel randomized controlled trial. *Cognitive Therapy and Research, 39*(1), 70–80.

White, N. D. (2015). Mindfulness-based cognitive therapy for depression, current episodes, and prevention of relapse. *American Journal of Lifestyle Medicine, 9*(3), 227–229. http://doi.org/10.1177/1559827615569677

Witkiewitz, K., & Black, D. S. (2014). Unresolved issues in the application of mindfulness-based interventions for substance use disorders. *Substance Use & Misuse, 49*(5), 601–604. http://doi.org/10.3109/10826084.2014.852797

Witkiewitz, K., Bowen, S., Harrop, E. N., Douglas, H., Enkema, M., & Sedgwick, C. (2014). Mindfulness-based treatment to prevent addictive behavior relapse: Theoretical models and hypothesized mechanisms of change. *Substance Use and Misuse, 49*(5), 513–524. http://doi.org/10.3109/10826084.2014.891845

Witkiewitz, K., Greenfield, B. L., & Bowen, S. (2013). Mindfulness-based relapse prevention with racial and ethnic minority women. *Addictive Behaviors, 38*(12), 2821–2824. http://doi.org/10.1016/j.addbeh.2013.08.018

Witkiewitz, K., Lustyk, M. K. B., & Bowen, S. (2013). Retraining the addicted brain: A review of hypothesized neurobiological mechanisms of mindfulness-based relapse prevention. *Psychology of Addictive Behaviors, 27*(2), 351–365. http://doi.org/10.1037/a0029258

Witkiewitz, K., Marlatt, G. A., & Walker, D. (2005). Mindfulness-based relapse prevention for alcohol and substance use disorders. *Journal of Cognitive Psychotherapy, 19*(3), 211–228. http://doi.org/10.1891/jcop.2005.19.3.211

Witkiewitz, K., Warner, K., Sully, B., Barricks, A., Stauffer, C., Thompson, B. L., & Luoma, J. B. (2014). Randomized trial comparing mindfulness-based relapse prevention with relapse prevention for women offenders at a residential addiction treatment center. *Substance Use and Misuse, 49*(5), 536–546.

Zeng, X., Li, M., Zhang, B., & Liu, X. (2015). Revision of the Philadelphia Mindfulness Scale for measuring awareness and equanimity in Goenka's Vipassana meditation with Chinese Buddhists. *Journal of Religion and Health, 54*(2), 623–637. http://doi.org/10.1007/s10943-014-9870-y

Zgierska, A., Rabago, D., Chawla, N., Kushner, K., Koehler, R., & Marlatt, A. (2009). Mindfulness meditation for substance use disorders: A systematic review. *Substance Abuse, 30*(4), 266–294. http://doi.org/10.1080/08897070903250019

Zgierska, A., Rabago, D., Zuelsdorff, M., Coe, C., Miller, M., & Fleming, M. (2008). Mindfulness meditation for alcohol relapse prevention: A feasibility pilot study. *Addiction, 2*(3), 165–173. http://doi.org/10.1097/ADM.0b013e31816f8546

Zylowska, L., Ackerman, D. L., Yang, M. H., Futrell, J. L., Horton, N. L., Hale, T. S., … Smalley, S. L. (2008). Mindfulness meditation training in adults and adolescents with ADHD a feasibility study. *Journal of Attention Disorders, 11*(6), 737–746. http://doi.org/10.1177/1087054707308502

7

Appendix: Tools and Resources

Mindfulness Practice Record

Date	Formal Practice	Mindfulness of Daily Activities	Comments
	Time start: _____ Time end: _____ Practice:	Activities:	
	Time start: _____ Time end: _____ Practice:	Activities:	
	Time start: _____ Time end: _____ Practice:	Activities:	
	Time start: _____ Time end: _____ Practice:	Activities:	
	Time start: _____ Time end: _____ Practice:	Activities:	

From: K. Witkiewitz, C. R. Roos, D. Dharmakaya Colgan, & S. Bowen: *Mindfulness*   © 2017 Hogrefe Publishing

Body Scan Meditation

Note: The following meditation instructions are provided only as an example. Facilitators are strongly encouraged to develop their own style of leading meditations by drawing from their own meditation practice and training, rather than reading from a script. Please see Section 4.2.4 for further details on guiding meditation practices.

To begin, find a comfortable position. You can lie down on the floor, sit in a chair, or choose another position that works best for you and your body. For this practice, we will bring our attention to various parts of our bodies, one at a time, noticing what sensations are present with an attitude of openness and curiosity. Closing your eyes if you wish or perhaps having your eyes open or half open and softening your gaze.

Bring your attention to the bottoms of your feet. Perhaps feeling your socks or shoes in contact with the soles of your feet. Acknowledging any sensations that you notice. Warmth, coolness, tingling, whatever it may be. And now, noticing the toes and the spaces between the toes, the tops of your feet, and the ankles.

Moving up to the lower legs, the shins and the calf muscles. Perhaps feeling your pants in contact with your skin. Tuning into any sensations that arise. Shifting your attention to your knees, the knee-caps, and the bottoms of the knees. Gently guiding your attention to your upper legs, the thighs and the hamstrings. You might notice pressure, tingling, tension, coolness, warmth, or itchiness.

And now, bringing your attention to your belly, feeling any movement of the breath in this area. Perhaps feeling your shirt in contact with your belly. You may find that your mind wanders off at times – planning, worrying, or daydreaming. Each time you notice your mind wandering, recognize what is on your mind in that moment, and then gently return your attention to your body. Acknowledging any thoughts or emotions as they arise and letting them be, and coming back to your body in this present moment.

Now, letting your attention travel to the lower back, opening to any sensations here, and experimenting with breathing into any sensations of tension or stiffness. Doing the best you can to just allow your body to feel the way it feels in this moment. Bringing your awareness now to the upper back and the shoulder blades. Notice what sensations meet you here. Shifting to your neck and shoulders, and experimenting again with breathing into any sensations of tension or stiffness.

Shifting your attention to your chest, perhaps exploring whether you can feel your heart beat. And when you are ready, bringing your awareness slowly down your arms, noticing what position your arms are in. Coming to your hands, your palms, your fingers, the spaces between the fingers. Opening to any sensations that you notice. Now, redirecting your attention to the inside of your mouth, the top of the mouth, the bottom, your lips, the space between your lips, your jaw, cheekbones, your nostrils, left nostril, right nostril, your eyes, forehead, and the top of your head.

And now expanding your awareness and becoming aware of your entire body in this moment. Sensing into your whole body. Listening to whatever your body has to tell you at this time. When you are ready, opening your eyes if they were closed. Taking a final moment to notice how your body feels right now.

From: K. Witkiewitz, C. R. Roos, D. Dharmakaya Colgan, & S. Bowen: *Mindfulness*   © 2017 Hogrefe Publishing

Sitting Meditation

Note: The following meditation instructions are provided only as an example. Facilitators are strongly encouraged to develop their own style of leading meditations by drawing from their own meditation practice and training, rather than reading from a script. Please see section 4.2.4 for further details on guiding meditation practices.

Start in a comfortable seated position with an upright spine and relaxed shoulders. Try to take a moment to relax the muscles of your body around your spine. The goal is to find a comfortable posture in which you can be both relaxed and alert. Now from this position focus your attention on the sensations of breathing, try to bring your attention to wherever you feel those sensations most strongly. You might focus on the rising and falling sensations of the chest or abdomen. Or you may focus on the sensations of air entering and leaving the nostrils.

Just notice the sensations of breathing without attempting to alter or manipulate the pace or pattern of breathing. The goal is to just focus all of your attention on the bare sensations of the breath.

Inevitably you will find that your mind has wandered or that some sensations have pulled your attention away from your breath. Regardless of the distraction, just notice that you are distracted and bring your attention back to the sensations of the breath.

If you find yourself continuously distracted by your thoughts or other sensations then you may try holding your attention on the breath by making a small mental note of the sensations of breathing. "Rising…falling" or "in…out" or "all-the-way-in…all-the-way out."

Now moving from the physical sensations of breathing to attending to the touching sensations of sitting in your seat or your feet on the floor, you may notice the temperature of the room, or sounds, or other sensations. Just be present in the moment with whatever is happening.

The goal is to just be open to whatever sensations or emotions or thoughts that are happening. Be present with these sensations or emotions, without judging or holding too tightly on to the experience.

Inevitably you will find that your mind has wandered. Perhaps you are thinking about this experience or maybe you are obviously thinking of something else. Regardless of the distraction just notice that you are distracted and bring your attention back to the sensations of the present moment.

Again you may notice that your mind has wandered. Notice that you have been distracted and to the best of your ability bring your full awareness back to whatever is happening in the present moment.

When you are ready, opening your eyes if they were closed. Taking a final moment to notice the sensations of the present moment.

From: K. Witkiewitz, C. R. Roos, D. Dharmakaya Colgan, & S. Bowen: *Mindfulness*   © 2017 Hogrefe Publishing

Advances in Psychotherapy
Evidence-Based Practice

Past volumes at a glance:

Vol. 1: Bipolar Disorder by R. P. Reiser / L. W. Thompson / S. L. Johnson / T. Suppes **(2nd edition 2017)**

Vol. 2: Heart Disease by J. A. Skala / K. E. Freedland / R. M. Carney

Vol. 3: Obsessive-Compulsive Disorder by J. S. Abramowitz (out of print, replaced by Vol. 31)

Vol. 4: Childhood Maltreatment by C. Wekerle / A. L. Miller / D. A. Wolfe / C. B. Spindel

Vol. 5: The Schizophrenia Spectrum by W. D. Spaulding / S. M. Silverstein / A. A. Menditto **(2nd edition 2017)**

Vol. 6: Treating Victims of Mass Disaster and Terrorism by J. Housley / L. E. Beutler

Vol. 7: Attention-Deficit/Hyperactivity Disorder in Children and Adults by A. U. Rickel / R. T. Brown
(out of print, replaced by Vol. 33 and Vol. 35)

Vol. 8: Problem and Pathological Gambling by J. P. Whelan / T. A. Steenbergh / A. W. Meyers

Vol. 9: Chronic Illness in Children and Adolescents by R. T. Brown / B. P. Daly / A. U. Rickel

Vol. 10: Alcohol Use Disorders by S. A. Maisto / G. J. Connors / R. L. Dearing

Vol. 11: Chronic Pain by B. J. Field / R. A. Swarm

Vol. 12: Social Anxiety Disorder by M. M. Antony / K. Rowa

Vol. 13: Eating Disorders by S. W. Touyz / J. Polivy / P. Hay

Vol. 14: Suicidal Behavior by R. McKeon

Vol. 15: Substance Use Problems by M. Earleywine **(2nd edition 2016)**

Vol. 16: Elimination Disorders in Children and Adolescents by E. R. Christophersen / P. C. Friman

Vol. 17: Sexual Violence by W. R. Holcomb

Vol. 18: Depression by L. P. Rehm

Vol. 19: Hypochondriasis and Health Anxiety by J. S. Abramowitz / A. E. Braddock

Vol. 20: Public Health Tools for Practicing Psychologists by J. A. Tucker / D. M. Grimley

Vol. 21: Nicotine and Tobacco Dependence by A. L. Peterson / M. W. Vander Weg / C. R. Jaén

Vol. 22: Nonsuicidal Self-Injury by E. D. Klonsky / J. J. Muehlenkamp / S. P. Lewis / B. Walsh

Vol. 23: Growing Up with Domestic Violence by P. G. Jaffe / D. A. Wolfe / M. Campbell

Vol. 24: Generalized Anxiety Disorder by C. D. Marker / A. G. Aylward

Vol. 25: Sexual Dysfunction in Women by M. Meana

Vol. 26: Sexual Dysfunction in Men by D. L. Rowland

Vol. 27: Phobic and Anxiety Disorders in Children and Adolescents by A. E. Grills-Taquechel / T. H. Ollendick

Vol. 28: Language Disorders in Children and Adolescents by J. H. Beitchman / E. B. Brownlie

Vol. 29: Autism Spectrum Disorder by L. Joseph / L. V. Soorya / A. Thurm

Vol. 30: Headache by T. A. Smitherman / D. B. Penzien / J. C. Rains / R. A. Nicholson / T. T. Houle

Vol. 31: Obsessive-Compulsive Disorder in Adults by J. S. Abramowitz / R. J. Jacoby

Vol. 32: Binge Drinking and Alcohol Misuse Among College Students and Young Adults by R. P. Winograd / K. J. Sher

Vol. 33: Attention-Deficit / Hyperactivity Disorder in Children and Adolescents by B. P. Daly / A. K. Hildenbrand / R. T. Brown

Vol. 34: Women and Drinking: Preventing Alcohol-Exposed Pregnancies
by M. M. Velasquez / K. Ingersoll / M. B. Sobell / L. Carter Sobell

Vol. 35: Attention-Deficit / Hyperactivity Disorder in Adults by B. P. Daly / E. Nicholls / R. T. Brown

Vol. 36: Multiple Sclerosis by P. B. Werfel / R. E. Franco Durán / L. J. Trettin

Vol. 37: Mindfulness by K. Witkiewitz / C. R. Roos / D. Dharmakaya Colgan / S. Bowen

Prices: US $29.80 / € 24.95 per volume standing order price US $24.80 / € 19.95 per volume
(minimum 4 successive volumes) + postage & handling. Special rates for APA Division 12 and Division 42 members

www.hogrefe.com